THE
ILLUSTRATED ENCYCLOPAEDIA
OF ANIMAL LIFE

THE ANIMAL KINGDOM

The strange and wonderful ways of
mammals, birds, reptiles, fishes and
insects. A new and authentic natural
history of the wild life of the world

VOLUME 10

FREDERICK DRIMMER, M.A.
EDITOR-IN-CHIEF

GEORGE G. GOODWIN
*Associate Curator of Mammals,
The American Museum of Natural
History*

CHARLES M. BOGERT
*Curator of Amphibians and Reptiles,
The American Museum of Natural
History*

DEAN AMADON
E. THOMAS GILLIARD
*Associate Curators of Birds,
The American Museum of Natural History*

CHRISTOPHER W. COATES, *Curator*
JAMES W. ATZ, *Assistant Curator*
*Aquarium of The New York Zoological
Society*

JOHN C. PALLISTER
Research Associate, Insects, The American Museum of Natural History

ODHAMS BOOKS LIMITED, LONG ACRE, LONDON

Colour photographs supplied by members of The Free Lance Photographers Guild except as otherwise individually credited.

DIPPERS—THEY WALK UNDER WATER

Dippers or water ouzels appeal to our fancy chiefly because of their remarkable ability to walk under water. Not only are they capable of doing this—they seem to take keen delight in it. They like to spend their time in and along the borders of ice-cold "white-water" mountain streams, and snowy waterfalls up to an altitude of 11,500 feet—sometimes even higher. Indeed, they spend their lives in a strange, intimate relationship with such streams, where they fly strongly from rock to rock, often breaking forth in a series of shrill flight notes as though thrilled by their closeness to the roaring waters.

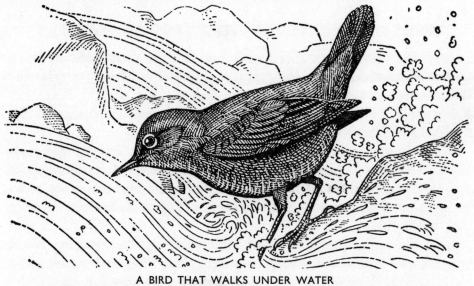

A BIRD THAT WALKS UNDER WATER

The dipper delights in the presence of water, and walks under the surface in quest of small creatures to feed on. So dense is the plumage of this thrush-sized bird that it can withstand temperatures of 50 degrees below zero.

While afoot, usually on water-washed rocks, the dipper sings a bubbling, wrenlike song. When hunting, the bird flicks its tail and often bobs into the water head first, sometimes submerging completely for many seconds. It walks along the bottom feeding on water beetles, caddis flies, dragonflies, and other water-dwelling insects. When the dipper swims on the surface, it paddles its feet alternately.

Dippers the world over—they comprise the family Cinclidae—are closely similar in structure and dress. All are the size of small thrushes, with stocky bodies, short tails, and thin straight bills. Predominantly greyish or brownish above, they sometimes have dark under parts

EAL / 10—A

—as in the American dipper, *Cinclus mexicanus*. In other dippers the under parts may be contrasted with buff or white on the chest and throat. As for their plumage, it is so dense and oily that dippers easily survive temperatures of 50° below zero in Alaska.

The dipper constructs its nest of grass and moss with a fine lining of leaves and rootlets. A domed affair with a narrow side-entrance, the nest is placed near water—on rocks, under bridges, or even on ledges behind waterfalls. The eggs are white. Dippers rear up to three broods a year, each of them from three to seven in number, often in the same nest.

WAGTAILS AND PIPITS—THEY SING AS THEY FLY

One of the members of this family has had the distinction of being starred in a full-length moving picture—probably the only songbird to be honoured in this way. This is the Tawny Pipit, *Anthus campestris*, a European bird and now perhaps the most noted member of the family Motacillidae.

Wagtails and pipits are slender, graceful birds famous for their habit of singing in flight. The great majority of the forty-five species are restricted to the Old World. The pipits, *Anthus*, are more widespread than their cousins, and two types of pipits make their home in North America.

Like the larks, longspurs, and some other ground-running birds, wagtails and pipits have a very long hind claw; their legs are long and slender. Many species have a habit of constantly wagging the tail up and down. Though these birds feed almost universally on the ground, a few have learned to run along horizontal tree limbs.

Wagtails are attractively coloured in black, white, and yellow. Pipits, on the other hand, have the streaked brownish plumage of typical grassland birds. The nest of these birds is an open cup, built of grass and rootlets, lined with hair and feathers, and placed on the ground. Four to six eggs are laid.

The Grey Wagtail, *Motacilla cinerea*, is a Eurasian bird resident in parts of Britain and usually found near water. In the Philippines we have watched it pacing nervously along the edges of swift mountain streams, feeding on water-dwelling insects. This predominantly greyish species is about eight inches long.

The Oriental Tree Pipit, *Anthus hodgsoni*, a bird of Asia and

Indo-Malaya, has moved its feeding niche from on or near the ground to the upper portions of forest trees. Near Baguio in the Philippines we saw it running like a squirrel along the horizontal branches of pine trees.

This species is olive brown, mottled with black above and pale buff below, with black spotting. Its length is about six inches.

AMERICAN PIPITS

The American Pipit, *Anthus spinoletta*, which nests on the Arctic tundra and above the treeline in the Rocky Mountains, may often be seen on open fields or along sandy shores throughout the United States when it is migrating. Despite this bird's dull olive-grey plumage, one can easily identify it by its high-pitched call note and restless habits.

The other American species is Sprague's Pipit, *Anthus spraguei*, discovered by Audubon on his expedition to the upper Missouri and called the "Missouri Skylark" because of its melodious song delivered from high in the air. This trait, you will recall, is one for which the lark is famous. The similarity in habits and appearance between larks and pipits is all the more remarkable since these birds are not related. On the wind-swept arid plains of Mexico we rarely saw Sprague's pipit until it jumped up from under foot with a sharp note of alarm and made off with rapid, erratic flight. This pipit has a habit of plummeting to earth so abruptly that only the most careful observation enabled us to mark where it landed.

OLD WORLD FLYCATCHERS

As you can tell from their name, these birds live in the Old World and they feed on insects. The family is a very large one, with 325 species—yet, not one of them is found in the Western Hemisphere! Among the most avid insect-chasers are a group called *Rhipidura* ("fantail"); they dwell in the Oriental and Australian regions. They are very tame birds, and one of them, the Australian Fantail, is an amusing creature on several counts. Its habit of constantly moving its tail has earned it the nickname of "Willie Wagtail". In its quest for flies, it even enters the doors or windows of buildings.

To aid them in engulfing their prey, flycatchers have broad, flat bills flanked by long bristles. Some flycatchers, however, pick insects from foliage or twigs; these have rather heavy, slightly hooked bills. It has probably occurred to you that these birds, which make up the family Muscicapidae, may be related to the New World Flycatchers, which have similar tastes in food; interestingly enough, the relationship, such as it is, is not particularly close.

Though a few flycatchers are found in the temperate parts of Eurasia, these are exceptional; the family is overwhelmingly tropical in distribution. Among the most striking are the Paradise Flycatchers— beautiful birds with flowing tail feathers about a foot long. The Indian Paradise Flycatcher, *Terpsiphone paradisi*, has black under-parts and a white back and tail. In Africa we find several related species which build a neat cuplike nest of moss and rootlets and lay from two to four spotted eggs.

As for the fantails, which we mentioned earlier, they are all very active in their pursuit of insects, seizing them with an audible snap of the bill.

In the pine forests close to the Philippine summer capital of Baguio we found a handsome Rufous and Blue Fantail, *Rhipidura cyaniceps*, one of the commonest and most attractive of the local birds. Other fantails have succeeded in colonizing the Pacific islands as far east as Guam and the Fijis. Fantails weave a neat cuplike nest and leave a dangling "tail" of loose fibres beneath it.

The Monarch Flycatchers (*Monarcha* and relatives) are even more prevalent in the Pacific—they have reached such remote islands as Tahiti. They are good-looking birds, with chestnut, white, and glossy black the main colours in their plumage.

Naturalists believe that the Hawaiian Elepaio, *Chasiempis sandwichensis*, belongs to the monarch flycatcher group. (Incidentally, the scientific name of this bird may strike you as queer unless you recall that the Hawaiian Islands used to be called the Sandwich Islands.) The elepaio is a very friendly and inquisitive bird—such a favourite, in fact, that the Hawaiian Audubon Society has named its journal *The Elepaio*.

Another group of Australian flycatchers has the curious name *Pachycephala* ("thickhead"), a reference to their rather heavy head and bill. Accomplished vocalists, they are also known as "whistlers". One species, *Pachycephala pectoralis*, has more geographical races or subspecies than any other bird—some eighty-odd are known! This clan is found throughout Australia, New Guinea, and most of the Pacific islands. Members of the group of shrike-billed flycatchers, these whistlers pick insects directly from foliage.

THRUSHES—SWEET SINGERS

The American Robin, *Turdus migratorius*, the most familiar of all native birds in most parts of the United States, is an outstanding member of the thrush family. Even in towns and cities you can often see this red-breasted thrush as it hops about on lawns in search of earthworms. It is interesting to watch a robin tugging and heaving to get the worm out of the ground. Some observers credit these birds with the ability to hear a worm stirring underground. The male robin looks very much like his mate, except that he is a little brighter below and darker on the head. As for the young, they are spotted with blackish marks on the breast when they are ready to leave the nest. We find such spotting in almost all young thrushes; it helps distinguish them from some of the related families, such as the Old World warblers and flycatchers.

The robin's nest is a sturdily built structure of mud and grass placed on the branch of a tree or even upon window sills or other ledges of buildings. Robins seem to take rather a casual attitude toward the problem of choosing a site for the nest; where it is not hidden or inaccessible, the young fall victim to cats and other enemies. Still, the species flourishes—apparently because it raises two or three broods a year. The colour of the eggs is the well-known "robin's-egg blue".

The song of the robin is famous for its cheerful quality—a loud, clear carol that may suggest a military air to you. But let its nest or young be threatened and the robin protests with strident chirps, calling the attention of all and sundry to its plight. In addition to worms, insects are the robin's favourite food; however, it has an unfortunate partiality for fruit which sometimes makes it a nuisance in cherry orchards.

MIGRATION

In the mountains of the West, the robin nests as far south as Mexico. Formerly it did not nest in most of the Southern United States, but in recent years it has been showing a tendency to nest in the south-east. While some robins are willing to brave the rigours of winter weather, the great majority migrate south. At that time of the year they assemble each night in vast numbers to roost. Up to 1913, when they received protection, the birds were sometimes shot for food at such roosts.

OTHER INTERESTING THRUSHES

There are some three hundred kinds of thrushes, making up the family Turdidae, and many of them are native to America. Of these latter, the best loved is the Bluebird, *Sialia sialis*. Of purest sky-blue above and tinged with chestnut below, it has gentle habits and soft warbling notes that endear it to all countryfolk. Normally the bluebird places its nest in a hollow stump but it will nest in such sites as a dilapidated country mailbox. The starling, introduced from Europe, often drives bluebirds from their nesting burrows and sometimes kills them with a blow of its bill.

The Mountain Bluebird, *Sialia currucoides*, which dwells in the Rocky Mountain area, is uniformly blue throughout. A somewhat similar—though larger—related species, *Grandala coelicolor* ("heavenly colour"), frequents the remote mountain fastnesses of western China and Tibet.

Unlike the bluebirds, the American thrushes of the genus *Hylocichla* are birds of modest yet pleasing brown and white colouring. The group includes the Wood Thrush, the Hermit Thrush, the Veery, and the Olive-backed Thrush—all of them exceptional songsters. The clear, bell-like notes of the wood thrush, which you can often hear within the limits of suburban towns, are considered by some the finest song of any American bird. Quite different is the veery's song with its wild, vibrating cadence. The European Nightingale, *Luscinia*, is closely related to the American thrushes we have just mentioned, and like them it is a bird of rather sombre plumage yet superb powers of song. As is well known, it sings mostly at night.

Still another melodious American thrush is the Townsend Solitaire, *Myadestes townsendi*, a bird of the Rocky Mountains region. Its pure notes are especially appealing in the wilderness where it dwells during the nesting season. Even near its home the solitaire is shy and retiring. We once found its nest on a rocky ledge above a beaver pond in the Medicine Bow Mountains of Wyoming. Though the nest held half-grown young, the parents made no outcry when we visited it and they usually remained out of sight.

When the early American colonists named the native robin after the Old World Robin Redbreast, *Erithacus rubecula*, they made a mistake which has continued to flourish for centuries. True, robin redbreast is also a thrush, but it is much smaller than the American robin and its habits are quite different.

The True Robin, or robin redbreast, is familiar to everyone, with its red breast and its cheeky manner. When you are digging in the garden a robin will often perch a few feet away, watching you while you work. Robins are not so friendly to other robins, however; a robin has his "territory" marked out exactly, and no other robin but his mate is allowed to enter it.

A FAMOUS THRUSH OF INDIA

The thrush family is noted for beautiful singing and this is especially true of the shama thrush, which dwells in the streamside thickets and jungles of India. Its song is usually heard at dawn and again at the close of day.

Among the many characteristic thrushes of the Old World are the wheatears. One species, the Greenland Wheatear, *Oenanthe leucorrhoa*, barely enters North America at each of its northern corners, Greenland and Alaska. Many other wheatears live in the deserts of the Middle East and Africa. Most of them have conspicuous white rumps and black marks on the head and throat.

The Redstarts, *Phoenicurus*, are another group of Old World thrushes.

One of them, the Black Redstart, though formerly very rare in the British Isles, has found the bombed-out ruins of blitzed cities to its liking and now nests in some numbers amid those desolate surroundings, where they still exist.

BABBLING THRUSHES—NOISY
BUT MELODIOUS

From a name like "babbler" you would conclude, rightly, that these birds are usually noisy. So they are—yet some of them are pleasing songsters. This Old World family is very large, with its 260 or so members. Most babblers live in undergrowth or on the ground. They are generally of medium or small size, but a few are as large as jays. As a rule their colours match the brush and undergrowth, though some of them have bright red patches in the wing, or other touches of colour.

The most interesting members of this family (Timaliidae) include the laughing thrushes of the genus *Garrulax*, which occur in great variety in the Himalayas. One species, the Song-babbler, *Garrulax canorum*, has been brought to the Hawaiian Islands and is now well established there. We found it to be a fine songster with rich alto notes. In form and habits it reminds us of the American thrashers. Another introduced babbler now common in Hawaii is the so-called Pekin Nightingale, *Liothrix lutea*. It utters a *churring* alarm note as it swarms through the undergrowth; the song is quite melodious.

Another variety, the parrot bill, creates problems. Naturalists used to place these birds with the titmice, but today the parrot bills are believed to be babblers. Actually, the parrot bills may be a link between the titmice and the babblers. Some parrot bills are partial to reed beds in swamps. This is true of the Bearded Titmouse, *Panurus*, the only babbler in the British Isles or, for that matter, in most of Europe. This bird's scientific name is interesting—like "the great God Pan" it is found among the reeds.

Another outlying parrot-bill babbler is the curious Wren Tit, *Chamaea fasciata*. Some naturalists believe that this Californian bird is the only American babbler, with relatives no nearer than faraway China. Like most members of the family, it builds a simple cuplike nest placed in low bushes. The eggs are pale blue and unspotted.

As for the family as a whole, babblers are related to thrushes but usually have stronger legs and shorter, more rounded wings. The young are not spotted. It is interesting to note that babblers stand in much the same relation to Old World thrushes as do thrashers and mocking-birds in the New World.

KINGLETS, GNATCATCHERS, AND OLD WORLD WARBLERS

Among the oddities of this fascinatingly diverse family are the Tailor-bird, which sews with the dexterity of a trained seamstress, the Cane-grass Warbler, the tiny gnatcatchers and kinglets and the equally tiny but far more brilliantly coloured Wren Warbler of Australia and New Guinea. Prominent among the almost four hundred species are the warblers found in Europe, and the common names of some of them will give you a good idea of their haunts and habits: Garden Warbler, Blackcap, Barred Warbler, Reed Warbler, Marsh Warbler, Sedge Warbler, Melodious Warbler, Willow Warbler, and Wood Warbler. Two that are named amusingly for their songs are the Grass-hopper Warbler and the Chiffchaff.

The Striated Canegrass Warbler, *Megalurus palustris*, a Philippine bird, is ten inches long and the largest member of this family (Sylviidae). This "giant" warbler lives in reed beds and in deep grass among bushes and thickets.

Its plumage is essentially the colour of dead grass, brownish with white striping and dull grey under-parts. This warbler utters its beautiful song—a melodious whistle—as it flies excitedly upwards from its perch. The ball-shaped nest, fastened to tall grass stems over dry ground, has a side entrance.

The common Tailorbird of the Philippines, *Orthotomus atrogularis*, is a nervous little creature of the bamboo thickets and forest edge. It is famous for its habit of stitching the edges of several large leaves together with strands of grass and thus forming a pocket in which its nest is placed. This species of tailorbird, which has relatives in Africa and Indo-Malaya, has olive-coloured upper parts with a reddish-brown crown and tail. The wings are greenish, the under-parts whitish.

The Alaska Willow Warbler, *Phylloscopus borealis kennicotti*, is the only Old World warbler of its clan to reach the New World, and even so it winters in the Eastern Hemisphere. In its winter habitat we have found it in small flocks feeding quietly in the topmost leaves of the forest canopy on Luzon in the Philippines. A tiny green warbler, it is practically indistinguishable in the field from many related species.

The Golden-crowned Kinglet, *Regulus satrapa*, and the Ruby-crowned Kinglet, *Regulus calendula*, are both New World birds. They belong to the subfamily Regulinae, which has seven species in all and ranges as far north as there are trees. Both New World kinglets are tiny olive-green birds that flit nervously about in the middle and upper branches of orchard and woodland trees. Very tame, they have the distinctive habit of constantly flicking their wings. The ruby-

THE RUBY-CROWNED KINGLET—A NOTABLE SONGSTER

Though not so famous as the nightingale or the lark, the ruby-crowned kinglet is one of the outstanding songsters of the bird world. Despite its nervous mannerisms, this small bird is surprisingly tame. The crest is erected only when the kinglet is excited.

crowned kinglet is endowed with powers of song far out of proportion to its diminutive size; indeed, we may class it among the great songsters. Kinglets nest in the north, wintering in the United States and south to Mexico and Guatemala. They lay five to ten whitish eggs sprinkled with brown or purple; their nests, little baskets of moss lined with rootlets and feathers, are suspended above the ground in cone-bearing forests.

The Blue-grey Gnatcatcher, *Polioptila caerulea*, is one of a dozen or so New World species that make up the subfamily Polioptilinae. A tiny bird with a long tail, it has a weak but elaborate song. Its nest, placed on the limb of a forest tree, is made of grass, beautifully decorated with lichens. Four or five whitish eggs, heavily marked with brown spots, are laid. Related gnatcatchers make their home in the thorny brush of the south-western deserts. As they flit from bush to bush they utter grating, wrenlike notes.

Most members of the Sylviidae are small, rather inconspicuous denizens of forest cover—grass, bushes, or trees. All feed on insects. Though one of the most important Old World families, the Sylviidae are represented in America, as we have seen, only by a few kinglets and gnatcatchers. The Old World warblers are very closely related to the babblers and Old World flycatchers. We have also noted that the Old World warblers are excellent songsters. In this respect they differ from the unrelated wood warblers of America (Parulidae), which usually have weak songs. We can distinguish the Sylviidae from the Parulidae in several other ways—the former have fluffier, more hairlike plumage, they possess ten instead of nine primary feathers, and they are usually given to drab colouring.

CHICKADEES AND TITMICE

The Black-capped Chickadee, *Parus atricapillus*, is one of the best-loved American birds. Chickadees are very friendly and inquisitive little birds. With even slight encouragement they will come to hand to secure sunflower seeds or peanuts, although they feed mostly on small insects and their eggs. These they can find even during the winter, so they do not migrate to any appreciable extent. Many people put out food (suet or sunflower seeds) for them in the wintertime. Even in bitter, snowy weather small flocks of them flit through the woods, as cheerful as ever. They assume all sorts of acrobatic poses in their search for food.

The chickadee is grey above and whitish below, and you can easily recognize it by its famous black cap and black throat. "Chickadee" is a good rendition of its call note. During the nesting season this bird utters a clear, pleasant two-syllabled whistle, sounding like "pee-wee". Beginners at bird study often assume this to be the note of the phoebe, which, as we know, is a flycatcher.

In the spring the sociable flocks of chickadees break up into pairs.

Each pair chooses a rotten stump in some secluded woodland and digs a hole in which the seven or eight spotted eggs are laid. They also roost in these holes on cold winter nights. We find a close relative of the black-capped chickadee in the Old World; it is known as the Willowtit. This is the bird that inspired the well-known song in *The Mikado*.

OTHER NOTEWORTHY TITMICE AND THEIR KIN

The Tufted Titmouse, *Parus bicolor*, is slightly larger than the chickadee and more plain coloured. Uniformly grey, it has a reddish wash on the sides, and a jaunty, pointed crest. The tufted titmouse is of rather southern distribution, ranging north to New Jersey. A closely related species, the Grey Titmouse, lives in the West. The prettiest member of the chickadee and titmouse family (Paridae) is the Old World Blue Titmouse, *Parus caerulus*. It is a charming little bird, with pastel shades of blue and yellow predominating in its plumage.

HANGING NESTS

In south-western United States and Mexico we find the tiny Bush-tit, *Auriparus minimus* ("smallest"), a plain-coloured bird that moves through the thorny desert brush in small flocks. An incessant chipping calls attention to their progress. These birds build a long baglike sack for their nest.

Another south-western species is the Yellow-headed Verdin, *Auriparus flaviceps*, a greyish-green bird with a yellow head. The verdin lacks the confiding, pleasant habits of most of its cousins. Instead, it flits nervously about and scolds loudly as soon as anyone approaches its domain. Naturalists believe that the verdin is related to the Penduline Titmice, *Remiz*, an Old World group, which get their name from their habit of weaving penduline (hanging) nests. Some of the African species weave their nests so skilfully that the finished product resembles heavy felt. The spoutlike entrance to these nests is on the side and is sometimes protected by a soft overhanging projection which the bird pushes aside each time it enters or leaves!

NUTHATCHES—OCCASIONALLY NUTCRACKERS

The White-breasted Nuthatch, *Sitta carolinensis*, a common bird in most parts of the United States, feeds mostly on small insects and their eggs and larvae. However, it also opens nuts by the ingenious method of jamming them into a crevice and then cracking ("hatcheting") them with repeated blows of its strong, pointed beak. The name "nuthatch" refers to this habit.

You can immediately recognize the white-breasted nuthatch by certain distinctive traits. Grey above and white below, it patrols the trunks and limbs of trees in search of insects. This may remind you of the woodpeckers and creepers, but the nuthatch differs from these birds by using only its feet—not its tail—in clinging to the bark. This gives it far more freedom of action, and it can hop head-first down tree trunks with ease. We have even seen the Philippine Coral-billed Nuthatch, *Sitta frontalis*, hanging from the bottom of a branch with one foot while it scratched itself with the other foot.

MUD NESTS

The white-breasted nuthatch selects a natural crevice in a tree and enlarges it as much as necessary to form a chamber for its eggs and young. Some of the Old World nuthatches plaster mud around the entrance to the nest cavity until just enough room remains for the birds to squeeze by. Thus squirrels and other enemies are foiled. The nut-hatches of the Persian deserts build their nests entirely of mud; attached to a rock, these nests may weigh as much as fifty pounds. Nuthatches make up the family Sittidae.

OTHER COLOURFUL NUTHATCHES

The Red-breasted Nuthatch, *Sitta canadensis*, a more northern bird than its white-breasted cousin, has a white-striped head, reddish flanks, and higher-pitched call notes. During the nesting season it prefers heavy evergreen forests, but while migrating it frequents orchards and parks.

The only other American species are the little Pigmy Nuthatch, *Sitta pygmaea*, a western bird, and the Brown-headed Nuthatch of the South-east. These sociable little nuthatches roam about the forests in little groups, incessantly uttering their harsh nasal calls; nuthatches do not sing.

The Tree-runners of Australia, *Neositta*, look like nuthatches and behave like them. However, the tree-runners differ in their nesting habits and may be unrelated to the nuthatches.

CREEPERS—THEY RARELY USE THEIR WINGS

The Brown Creeper, *Certhia familiaris,* is a far-ranging North American bird that typifies the true creepers. Its flight is weak and fluttering and is chiefly used to make short descents from the top of one tree to the base of another where it resumes its nervous, unending search for insects and their eggs and larvae which it gathers from crevices in bark. It sounds a soft lisping note as it spirals up the bark.

Many forms of this species make their home in the Northern Hemisphere—there are groups of creepers in the British Isles, Japan, and in North America, and all told they comprise the family Certhiidae. More slender and smaller than a sparrow, this creeper is mainly bright brown with ochraceous white streaks and dull white under-parts. It has thin graduated tail feathers ending in woodpecker-like spines which help it in creeping up tree trunks. The bill is long, slender, and curved. The long sharp toes provide the creeper's feet with a firm grip as it climbs.

The brown creeper—the only true creeper in North America—has five relatives in Europe and Asia. However, naturalists include fifteen or so Old World birds in the family, although their relationship is not yet fully understood. All have the same general form and show similar feeding adaptations.

The brown creeper places its nest of bark, wool, moss, and twigs under a large, loose piece of bark. In late May it deposits five to eight white eggs, speckled and wreathed with reddish brown. Naturalists have found nesting creepers in the mountains as far south as North Carolina. The chief breeding range, however, is from the northern portions of the United States northward.

The Wall Creeper, *Tichodroma muraria,* which dwells in the Alpine regions of Eurasia, is a very beautiful bird. Seven inches long, it is the largest of the creepers. In its wings there are pretty patches of red, visible only when it is flying. When at rest, it appears dull grey with a black throat and chest. We are told that unlike other creepers, this bird has a melodious call. Feeding on spiders and insects, it lives in rocky areas, chiefly around cliffs, often reaching great altitudes in summer.

It builds a nest in rock cavities, constructing a cup of grass and moss where it lays three to four spotted eggs.

FLOWERPECKERS—THEY LIKE MISTLETOE

Flowerpeckers are very small birds, often brightly coloured with red or yellow. Noted for their active, sprightly habits, they are fond of the sticky berries of the parasitic mistletoe and are guilty of spreading the seeds of this harmful plant. They also eat small insects, nectar, and fruit.

The nest, which is usually a pear-shaped bag with a side entrance, is similar to nests of sunbirds, to which the flowerpeckers are related. The fifty or so species of flowerpeckers—they make up the family Dicaeidae—are best represented in the Orient, although several are found in New Guinea and Australia.

Perhaps the best-known flowerpecker is the Australian Mistletoe Bird, *Dicaeum hirundinaceum*. This tiny bird lives at the top of the tall eucalyptus trees, and its flight is very rapid and darting. Its nest is remarkably pretty—woven of soft cottony vegetable down and hanging from a branch as if the twigs had been pushed through it.

The curious little Australian Diamond Birds, *Pardalotus*, so called because their plumage is "spotted like the (leo)pard", are members of this family. Unlike other flowerpeckers, they hunt for insects in foliage and dig little tunnels in the ground in which to build their nests.

AUSTRALIAN HONEY EATERS

Hawaiian princes used to have their lovely feather capes made from the yellow and black feathers of a beautiful species of honey eater that is now extinct. The natives called it the "o-o" in imitation of its call.

Today the honey eaters, which compose the family Meliphagidae, are almost entirely confined to the Australian region. These birds have a long, tubular tongue for sucking nectar from flowers. The brushy tip of this tongue is sticky, enabling the honey eater to catch insects and spiders efficiently. Honey eaters are medium-sized or even large songbirds, usually marked with yellow and adorned with tufts of long yellow feathers or with wattles. We find these birds on many Polynesian islands.

The Tui or Parson Bird, *Prosthemadera*, one of the best known of New Zealand birds, is somewhat similar to the extinct species we mentioned earlier. Its dark metallic green plumage, set off by curling white feathers on the throat, inspired its popular name, "parson bird". Flitting rapidly about the branches of the forest, pecking here and there at an insect or diving its bill into the recesses of a newly opened flower, it continually utters a shrill, sharp whistle.

WHITE-EYES—AVID EATERS OF NECTAR

Naturalists have a hard time telling the nearly eighty species of white-eyes apart. Most of these birds are greenish with a silvery-white eye-ring, and are exasperatingly similar in appearance. The few which lack the white eye-ring look like small green warblers, and they are even more perplexing to identify.

White-eyes are sociable, active, restless, vireo-like birds; they make up the family Zosteropidae. We find them in Africa, Madagascar, southern Asia (north to Japan), and the Australian region. Despite the resemblances to various birds that we have noted, they are thought to have their closest kinship with the Australian honey eaters.

The Japanese White-eye, *Zosterops palpebrosa japonica*, is a good songster and is often kept as a cage bird. When released in the Hawaiian Islands by some of the Japanese colonists, it spread like wildfire and is now far more common than any of the native Hawaiian birds. On an estate in the Philippines we saw a large flock of golden-headed white-eyes feeding avidly on nectar obtained from the blossoms of an ornamental tree. To aid them in such feeding, many white-eyes have a tubular tongue. These birds also eat berries and doubtless some insects. Their nest is a cup swung in a horizontal fork, like the nest of an American vireo. The eggs are usually blue and unspotted.

SUNBIRDS—HUMMING-BIRDS OF THE OLD WORLD

It is not illogical to call sunbirds the humming-birds of the Old World, though the two groups are quite unrelated. Sunbirds fill the niche that humming-birds occupy in the New World tropics and resemble them in brilliance of plumage and in feeding habits. On the other hand, they do not have the humming flight of their American counter-parts, nor are they so small, ranging in size from four to eight inches. Males are often strikingly iridescent while the females and young are more drably coloured.

Sunbirds have a long, slender, curved bill. The tongue is tubular and extensible, a feature we have noted in humming-birds and others

A VICTIM OF LANGUAGE EVOLUTION

The tufted titmouse with his chestnut flanks and usually jauntily flaunted crest hardly seems one to be called "mouse", but the name "titmouse" derives from a combination of Anglo-Saxon and Middle English words meaning "a small thing". The pert little bird is native to the eastern United States, with the exception of certain localized areas. Titmice as a family have rather widespread distribution, and range in coloration from a pastel blue and yellow Old World species to the tiny drab bush-tit of the desert areas of south-western United States and Mexico.

See page 1142.

NOT ALL BLACKBIRDS ARE BLACK

The converse of this statement is also true—not all black birds are blackbirds, although the name is commonly used for numerous species the males of which are largely black or sufficiently sombre-hued as to be almost black. The male American red-wing, to which the name applies technically, is entirely black except for his brilliant epaulettes, but the brown and buff female with her spotted breast resembles an over-grown thrush. These two birds are more closely related to the orioles and meadowlarks than they are to the crows. *See page 1150.*

THE BEAUTIFUL LONG-TAILED SUNBIRD

Many members of the sunbird clan are strikingly handsome, but the long-tailed sunbird is
outstanding, with its glossy green head, shiny purple lower back and tail, and rich yellow
under-parts. This sunbird has very long middle tail feathers.

that feed on nectar. When feeding, sunbirds hover before a flower
like the humming-bird, or else they perch beside the blossom and
probe it for honey, small insects, and spiders.

We find the species of sunbirds, making up the family Nectariniidae,
in the warmer parts of the Old World. Their favourite haunts are
the middle and upper forest portions up to altitudes of five thousand
feet. Some species frequent bushes in native gardens. These birds
have a weak, sometimes melodious song, and they also utter a variety
of chipping notes. The sunbird's typical nest is a pear-shaped affair of
grass, moss, rootlets, and spider webbing. Beautifully camouflaged, this
hanging nest is often remarkable for a tubular, spoutlike side entrance
which sometimes resembles a tiny porch. The sunbird lays two or
three whitish or pastel-tinted eggs, sprinkled with many colours.

SPECTACULAR SUNBIRDS

The Malachite Sunbird of Africa, *Nectarinia famosa*, notable for
its brilliance and its greatly elongated central tail feathers, is one of

the most beautiful species. This is particularly true of the male, dressed in glistening iridescent green. The bird has a total length of about eleven inches, including the three inches of feathers that extend from the tail. The bill is long, slender, and curved.

Another spectacular member of the tribe is the Scarlet-chested Sunbird, *Chalcomitra senegalensis*, also of Africa. Six inches long, it is iridescent green on the forehead and sides of the face, with a scarlet lower throat and chest. The sprightly habits and colourful appearance of this bird and many of its cousins of the Old World tropics have won for them the appropriate name of "sunbirds".

The Grey-breasted Spider-hunter, *Arachnothera affinis*, which lives in south-east Africa, is an unusual bird—it builds an open, cuplike nest in tall plants near native habitation. These spider-hunters are about six inches long, with a long, heavy, black bill. The male is yellowish olive above, greyish brown below.

VIREOS—INCESSANT SINGERS AND SKILFUL BUILDERS

Perhaps you have heard of the "Brain fever" Bird, a small brush cuckoo of the Orient that sings incessantly at siesta time from a single perch, and is reputed to have driven men mad. We have no comparable tales about the vireos, but it is true that most of them have rather loud voices, and several species seem to sing almost continuously. The Red-eyed Vireo, for one, utters a monotonous chant from dawn to dark.

These warbler-like birds of woodland and brush are less nervous and jerky in their movements than warblers and their colouring is quieter and of more protective value. This exclusively American family (Vireonidae) contains forty-one or so species. For the most part they are small, olive or greyish-green birds which sometimes travel in the company of warblers. Feeding almost solely on insects and their larvae, they sometimes add berries to their menu in the autumn. Methodically they scan bark surfaces, small twigs, and leaf surfaces for food, and you may be sure that very little escapes their attention.

Vireos take great pains in building their nests. They all weave beautiful little hanging basket-like nests which are attached to horizontal forks. The nest locations may be as low as three feet from the ground, or as high as ninety feet. The usual nest material is grass, plant fibres, lichens, and spider webs; often the rim is decorated with fine moss.

Vireos lay four or five white eggs finely sprinkled with brown and black spots.

Vireos have a uniformity of habits that is remarkable considering their wide variety of favoured environments all the way from sea level to an altitude of nine thousand feet. Those that breed in the cooler portions of the Northern Hemisphere migrate into the tropics in winter. The most familiar and widespread member of the family is the Red-eyed Vireo, *Vireo olivaceus*. It can be seen wherever there are trees in any number, be they in parks, along roads, or in deep woodlands. Olive green or white below, it has a slate-grey cap bordered on either side with black. A white line runs over the eye, which is red in the adult, brown in the young birds.

A few tropical vireos, such as the so-called Pepper-Shrike, *Cyclarhis*, have an unusually heavy bill. In fact, there is some doubt whether they are vireos at all.

BOBOLINKS, BLACKBIRDS, MEADOWLARKS, ORIOLES, AND THEIR RELATIVES

The Bobolink, *Dolichonyx oryzivorus*, is one of the most popular birds over much of the eastern and central United States. Many consider it the best singer of all American songbirds. The ecstatic bird treats us to a bubbling, happy melody as he flies slowly with quivering wings above the hayfield where his mate is incubating her four to six eggs. The bobolink's nest is a flimsy grass cup, placed in a depression in the grass.

The male is a handsome bird, black below, black, white, and yellow above. His modestly coloured mate is streaked with buff and grey, closely matching the grassy fields where bobolinks dwell. With the coming of autumn the male, too, moults into this protective plumage. The bobolink is a great migrant, travelling all the way to the Argentine pampas to spend the winter. In former days, when much rice was grown in the Carolina lowlands, flocks of migrating bobolinks appeared in the autumn and ate their fill. In fact, the scientific name of this bird means "rice eater". The bobolink is perhaps the most outstanding bird of the family Icteridae, which also includes blackbirds, meadowlarks, orioles and other familiar birds.

The Eastern Meadowlark, *Sturnella magna*, and the **Western Meadowlark,** *Sturnella neglecta*, are so similar that you would find it difficult to tell them apart. One point of difference is that the western kind has a more melodious song. The male and female are nearly alike in colour. Streaked above for camouflage in the grass, they have a

THE BOBOLINK—ONE OF AMERICA'S MOST POPULAR BIRDS

The bobolink is one of the best-loved American birds. It is an ecstatic singer, and it is also one of the great migrating birds, wintering regularly on the Argentine pampas. It is sometimes called the ricebird.

bright-yellow breast and black bib. The outer feathers of the short, broad tail are white. The birds are quite noticeable as they take flight from a grassy field or twitch their tails nervously as they perch on a fence post. Meadowlarks are as chunky as quail, and have a somewhat similar flight—rapid bursts of wingbeats, followed by short glides. For this reason meadowlarks were formerly shot as game birds.

The Red-winged Blackbird, *Agelaius phoeniceus*, is probably one of the ten most abundant birds in the United States. The male is a handsome bird, glistening black with brilliant scarlet shoulder patches or epaulettes. In the spring he flaps slowly through the air to display these marks to his mate and to all others who may watch and admire. The song is a loud, mellow *kong-ka-ree*. In the autumn, this blackbird and other species gather in large flocks and are sometimes destructive to grain.

THE MEADOWLARK RELIES ON PROTECTIVE COLORATION

The meadowlark builds its nest on the ground and spends much of its time in grassy fields, where its streaked upper parts blend with its surroundings. This bird is a great destroyer of crop-damaging insects in summer; in winter it consumes weed seeds in large quantities. In flight, the white outer tail feathers are conspicuous.

The red-wing prefers marshes but has learned to nest even in dry hayfields, as two noted American naturalists, Theodore Roosevelt and John Burroughs, were the first to point out. The nest of the red-wing is a carefully woven cup suspended, as a rule, among reeds in a marsh. The eggs, like those of many of its relatives, are bluish white, marked with irregular blackish scrawls.

The Crow Blackbird or Grackle, *Quiscalus quiscula*, also a common bird in the United States, has a voice so squeaky that it has been likened to the creaking of a rusty gate. Almost as large as a blue jay, this bird has entirely black plumage, that of the male being highly irridescent, with bronzy, greenish, or purplish reflections in bright sunlight.

A less attractive bird than many of its cousins, the grackle sometimes kills the young of other birds by a blow of its heavy bill, and may also be destructive to grain.

In the southern swamps we find a related though larger species, the Boat-tailed Grackle, *Cassidix mexicanus*. The males are black, the females brownish, and the former are much larger. As we so often note about birds where this difference in size prevails, the male is polygamous. In Mexico the boat-tailed grackle is less limited to marshes than in the southern United States, and each little village or ranch has its noisy flock.

COWBIRDS—THE ONLY PARASITIC AMERICAN BIRDS

Very similar to blackbirds in appearance, cowbirds are nevertheless unique among American birds for their parasitic habits. For that matter, it is stretching a point to include the cowbird among the songsters, for the courtship call of the male is a very creaky whistle produced only at the expense of disproportionate effort and bodily contortion as he sits on a dead limb. The male Eastern Cowbird, *Molothrus ater*, is shiny black with a brown head; the female is dull greyish.

Stealthily the female cowbird seeks out the nests of smaller birds— song sparrows, ovenbirds, yellow warblers, vireos, and many others. Then, early in the morning, she slips on to the nest and lays one of her own eggs. The morning before doing this, she usually removes one of the eggs of her victim by puncturing it with her bill and carrying it off. As a rule she lays only one egg in a nest, seeking another nest for the next egg.

Usually the victimized bird does not object to the strange egg and incubates it with her own. The young cowbird is almost always bigger than its nest mates and with its greedy appetite monopolizes the food brought by the parents. The likely upshot is that the true young of the foster parents starve, and the parents are left with the single young cowbird, often twice their own size! Even so, the young cowbird continues to beg shamelessly for food for some time after leaving the nest.

The cowbird is a common species, with the result that in some areas as many as half the nests of song sparrows, ovenbirds, and others of its favoured victims suffer from its invasion of their homes. Thus you can see that the cowbird is responsible for the destruction of many young songbirds; but perhaps many of these would in any case represent surplus population. Dr. Herbert Friedmann made an interesting study of certain South American cowbirds in which parasitism is less perfected or entirely absent. By studying the behaviour of these birds, Dr. Friedmann was able to show how the parasitic habit has evolved.

The Baltimore Oriole, *Icterus galbula*, is a lovely orange and black bird. It gets its name from the fact that its colours are the same as those of the House of Baltimore, the patrons of the Colony of Maryland. Apart from its handsome appearance, the Baltimore oriole is also notable for its deep, carefully woven nest which is attached to the thin end twigs of a tree. The bird prefers the drooping branches of the American elm above all others. Grass is the normal weaving material but horsehair and string are sometimes used. Once in a while we find a dead oriole hanging near its nest with a loop of string or horsehair around its neck—a victim of its own industry.

Though orioles are the most numerous members of this family in the American tropics, the Baltimore oriole is the only species that is common in the northern United States. Less brightly coloured than her mate, the female still has enough orange hue in her plumage to be recognizable.

The song of the Baltimore oriole is a series of loud, clear whistles, pleasant though not particularly melodious.

We find other orioles in the southern and western regions of the United States. Almost all of them weave artistic nests which are sometimes sewn into or suspended between large leaves. One attractive lemon-yellow and black species, Scott's Oriole, *Icterus parisorum*, is partial to the yuccas of the rocky hillsides of Arizona and Mexico.

OROPENDOLAS AND THEIR HUGE NESTS

Oropendolas—the name is Spanish—are tropical relatives of the orioles. They build hanging nests which are sometimes as much as three feet long. As a rule the nests are swung from some lofty jungle tree.

Usually oropendolas nest in colonies. The males are larger than the females and, like the male cowbird, they make an acrobatic ritual out of uttering their gurgling courtship notes. Meanwhile the hardworking females weave the long swinging nests and raise the young. Some oropendolas are as large as a crow. They may be yellow or orange and black, like their close relatives the orioles, but some of the largest species have a greenish hue.

A BIRD THAT BUILDS LARGE SWINGING NESTS

The oropendola, a tropical cousin of the orioles, is famous for its huge hanging nest, which is sometimes as much as three feet long. All the credit for weaving these remarkable structures belongs to the female; her mate remains aloof from the work.

NEW WORLD WARBLERS

New World warblers are small birds—smaller than a sparrow—and most of them are brightly coloured. During their migrations as many as twenty or more different kinds of warblers may be seen in a single morning in the north-eastern United States. This variety makes them a favourite of bird students. Many of the warblers seen on these migrations have nested in Canada. On misty nights they sometimes lose their bearings and large numbers are killed when they strike such tall obstructions as the Empire State Building in New York. Naturalists know of some 110 species of the family, the Parulidae, which is found throughout North and South America.

The Yellow Warbler, *Dendroica aestiva,* is the best-known species. Entirely yellow, it is lightly streaked with dusky or reddish markings. It arrives in the spring about the time the apple trees are in bloom and quickly announces its presence by its loud song. Most warblers, by the way, have rather lisping, high-pitched songs. Though they are poor music, the songs are a great help when you try to identify the birds. People sometimes mistake yellow warblers for goldfinches ("wild canaries"). However, if you study both birds, you will see that the yellow warbler lacks the black and yellow plumage pattern and the heavy bill of the goldfinch.

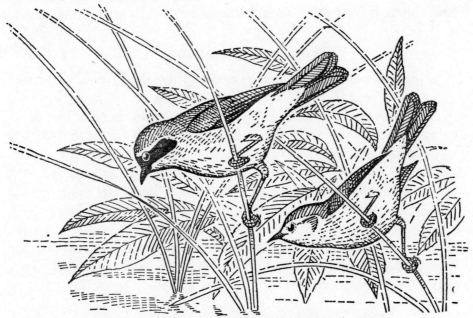

A WOOD WARBLER THAT DOES NOT LIVE IN THE WOODS
The yellow-throat, found throughout North America, lives in grass and weeds near streams. The black-masked male repeatedly utters his loud song, which sounds like "witchety, witchety, witchety". This bird builds its nest on or near the ground in a clump of grass.

The yellow warbler builds a neat cuplike nest of plant down and rust-coloured fern fibres in which it lays four olive-spotted eggs. The parasitic cowbird, as we have seen, often lays one of its eggs in the nest of the yellow warbler. Sometimes the victimized bird may react resourcefully by building a new bottom in its nest to cover up the alien egg and start again with its own egg laying.

Like most members of this family, the yellow warbler feeds almost entirely on insects.

Among the relatives of the yellow warbler there are several that deserve mention. One of these is the Redstart, *Setophaga ruticilla*, a beautiful warbler with orange and black plumage. When pursuing a flying insect it has a tumbling butterfly-like flight that gives it the appearance of a streak of flame in the forest gloom. That is why the Cubans, who know this bird only as a winter visitor, call it the *candelita* ("little candle").

The Yellow-throat, *Geothlypis trichas*, favours tall grass and low bushes in marshes. Male and female are yellow, but the male has black masklike areas on the sides of the head. The yellow-throat's song is a loud "wichety" repeated several times.

GROUND WARBLERS

The ground warblers are well represented by the Ovenbird, *Seiurus aurocapillus* ("gold cap"). This bird should not be confused with the tropical Ovenbirds (Furnariidae), which we discussed earlier. The ovenbird of the warbler family has a brown back and white under-parts spotted with brownish black. There is a golden area on the crown, but you can rarely see it. The ovenbird has yellow legs and, like the other ground warblers, it walks rather than hops. Its nest, roofed over like an oven, is made of grass and leaf stems on the forest floor. The ovenbird has a very loud song, resembling the word "teacher" repeated over and over with increasing emphasis. At twilight the ovenbird flutters above the lower trees and offers a sweet flight song.

COUSIN OF THE OVENBIRD

The Louisiana Water Thrush, *Seiurus motacilla*, is, despite its deceptive common name, a cousin of the ovenbird. Partial to deep rocky glens or ravines, this water thrush builds its nest in a little depression in a stream bank. The Northern Water Thrush, *Seiurus noveboracensis*, has a wider range. During its migrations it may be found along the edges of streams or ponds. Like many other birds of similar habits

—even such totally unrelated ones as the spotted sandpiper or "tip-up" —the common water thrush is given to incessantly teetering up and down.

HAWAIIAN HONEY CREEPERS—VERSATILE BIRDS

When the celebrated explorer Captain James Cook discovered the Hawaiian Islands in 1778, he found the native princes wearing red, yellow, and orange robes made of the feathers of birds. These colourful cloaks were assembled from the feathers of the Hawaiian honey creepers, a family found only on these islands.

Among biologists, the Hawaiian honey creepers have long been famous as an example of "adaptive radiation" or "divergent evolution". To put it briefly, the structure of these birds has changed, depending on their ways of getting food. Thus, some of them have long, curved bills for sucking nectar from flowers; some are heavy-billed seed-eaters; still others are modified in many ways for feeding on insects. Since very few songbirds ever reached the Hawaiian Islands, this family (the Drepaniidae) was free to diversify and utilize the many sources of food available on these tropical islands. But living in isolation has its seamy side as well. About half of the twenty-two species of Hawaiian honey creepers are now extinct—they proved all too susceptible to diseases brought by birds introduced by man on the islands.

HONEY CREEPERS—THEY COMPETE WITH HUMMING-BIRDS

Honey creepers are birds with curved bills and long, tubular tongues adapted for feeding on the nectar and tiny insects found in flowers. Perhaps because they must compete with the humming-birds, we find that the American honey creepers are much fewer in number of species—only thirty-five or so, making up the family Coerebidae— than their Old World counterparts, the sunbirds and Australian honey eaters.

Like many birds that feed on nectar and frequent the outer, sunnier portions of jungle trees, honey creepers are often brightly coloured. The Blue Honey Creeper, *Cyanerpes cyaneus*, has black wings, tail, and shoulders; the rest of the body is a bright, glistening blue. The common Bananaquit, *Coereba flaveola*, a bird of the West Indies and

South America, is greyish above and yellow below, with prominent white lines over the eyes.

Most honey creepers build a domed nest with a side entrance. This nest is more of a home than most bird nests, for the honey creeper sometimes roosts in it, apart from using it for its eggs.

TANAGERS—COLOURFUL BIRDS

With its brilliant scarlet body and black flight plumes, the Scarlet Tanager, *Piranga olivacea*, is a typical member of the colourful family Thraupidae. As with many other kinds of tanagers, there is quite a difference in colouring between the sexes. The male is vividly dressed, the female is sombre in appearance, green being a frequent colour.

Closely akin to the finches, tanagers are usually thrush-sized, though a few reach the proportions of a starling or jay. Most tanagers have weak voices, but some species—the scarlet tanager is one of them —have pleasant songs. Tanagers frequently congregate in large mixed parties to feed—chiefly on insects and fruit which they gather in the forest. For the most part they live in trees; a few, shy and retiring, live on or near the ground in forests where they scratch for food like large sparrows or towhees. Contrast this with such species as the Bishop Tanager, *Thraupis episcopus*, of South America, which spend their noisy group existence close to man. Frequently the second type is found in city parks and about suburban homes.

While a few tanagers make ball-like domed nests, the typical tanager nest is a shallow structure of twigs lined with fibres and leaves, placed four to thirty feet above the ground in saplings. Two to four bluish or greenish-white eggs are laid. The great majority of the nearly two hundred species of tanagers dwell in the forests of the American tropics, with some reaching Canada and Chile.

Four tanagers breed in the United States but return to warmer climes in winter.

Apart from the scarlet tanager, the only other species found in the eastern United States is the Summer Tanager, *Piranga rubra*; the male is a beautiful rosy-red bird. The Western Tanager, *Piranga ludoviciana*, which substitutes for the scarlet tanager in the west, is bright yellow with black wings and tail and much scarlet on the neck and head. One of the most vividly coloured of the tribe is the tropical

Paradise Tanager, *Tanagra chilensis.* Its velvety-black upper parts are contrasted with glistening apple green on the head, scarlet on the lower back, yellow on the rump, glossy opal blue on the under-parts, and purple on the throat, neck, and bend of the wing.

A BRILLIANT BIRD OF NORTH AMERICA

The scarlet tanager, with its vivid scarlet body and black wings and tail, is one of the most brilliant birds of North America. The female, generally green, is not nearly so spectacular as her colourful mate. Interestingly enough, the male discards his striking plumage after the mating season, assuming a green garb very similar to the female's. Caterpillars and other slow insects are a favourite food of the scarlet tanager.

Some South American tanagers are quite extraordinary, as, for example, the Violaceous Euphonia, *Tanagra violacea.* No bigger than a tiny finch, this bird has purplish-blue upper parts and orange under-parts. Some of these little euphonia tanagers live on the sticky covering of the berries of the parasitic mistletoe. The euphonia tanager is radically modified in order to consume this fare—instead of the stomach and gizzard found in other birds, it has a straight tube to permit ready passage of the seeds.

SWALLOW-TANAGERS

This South American bird, which looks like a cotinga, is apparently related to the tanagers. However, naturalists have placed the swallow-tanager in a separate family (Tersinidae), partly because its skull structure has some unusual features, partly because it differs from the true tanagers in nesting in a burrow or hollow tree. The male swallow-tanager is greenish, tinged with beautiful opalescent blue and marked with wavy black lines. The female is more greenish.

PLUSH-CAPPED FINCHES

The Plush-capped Finch, *Catamblyrhynchus diadema*, is a curious little bird closely related to the tanagers and finches. It differs from them in having a crown capped with hair or spinelike plumes of a felt-like texture. There is only one species in this family (Catamblyrhynchidae) ranging from Venezuela to Bolivia in mountain forests where it is found in mixed flocks. The plush-capped finch has a black hind crown and maroon under-parts. So far as we know, no naturalist has ever found the nest or eggs of this bird.

A BILL THAT CRACKS CHERRY STONES

A handsome study in pinkish brown, black, and chestnut is the hawfinch, a robustly built European member of the finch family. This bird, like its American cousin the evening grosbeak, has a huge bill. While it can crack cherry stones with ease, the hawfinch also consumes softer foods, such as green peas.

FINCHES, BUNTINGS, GROSBEAKS, AND RELATED BIRDS

With its 425 or so species, the finches and their numerous cousins make up the largest of all bird families. What is even more interesting is that the great Darwin's epoch-making work on evolution was inspired by his observations of a group of finches. This was how it happened: as a young man, Darwin took an assignment as naturalist on the famous voyage of H.M.S. *Beagle.* One of the most important stops made by the expedition was at the desolate, lava- and cactus-covered Galápagos Islands, lying about six hundred miles off the

THE GOLDFINCH OR "WILD CANARY"

The goldfinch, a cousin of the tame canary, is famed for its lovely call; *perchickoree, perchickoree* is what it sounds like. This bird's menu consists largely of dry plant fruits and seeds. The less brilliantly coloured female (*left*) feeds her four to six babies with seeds which she has predigested for them.

coast of Ecuador. Here the young scientist came across a clan of finches called Geospizas or ground finches.

Every island in the group has a number of species of these unimpressive black or greyish birds. Often the species differ in little except the size of the bill. In trying to understand this variation, Darwin was led to speculate on evolution and the origin of species. That is why these birds are sometimes called "Darwin's finches".

Since finches are so diverse and dwell in all parts of the world, they still offer naturalists many problems. Generally speaking, finches —they make up the family Fringillidae—are small or medium-sized songbirds; very few are as large as the American robin. Their colour patterns are endlessly varied; some are protectively coloured, others are bright red or yellow. Many finches—the domestic canary, for example—are beautiful songsters.

The Goldfinch, *Spinus tristis* ("sad"), is a handsome black and yellow bird that makes its home in North America. It nests rather tardily, from late June to August, building its nest largely of thistledown. The male has a lovely flight song. The call-note of the goldfinch is tinged with melancholy, hence its scientific name. In flight the goldfinch undulates up and down in the air, as though riding a roller coaster. Though it resembles a canary, the latter was derived from an Old World species.

The Common Crossbill, *Loxia curvirostra*, and the **White-winged Crossbill,** *Loxia leucoptera*, are both deep wine red, but the latter bird has white wing bars. In both birds we find that the sharp tips of the jaws cross and overlap. This is an adaptation for opening the cones of evergreens to secure the little seeds beneath the scales. While doing this, crossbills hold the cones in their feet, parrot-wise, and twist off the scales rapidly and efficiently with their unique bill.

The Song Sparrow, *Melospiza melodia*, is perhaps the best known of the numerous North American sparrows or buntings, thanks to the extensive studies Mrs. Margaret M. Nice has made of these birds. She has found that each pair has a territory in which the nest is located. The male's song tells other male song sparrows that he is in possession of a nesting territory and will brook no intrusion. The song also attracts a mate to his territory. We encounter such "territorialism" with many other birds. It is probably an adaptation to

[10-1]

If the American robin is the best-known American thrush, the bluebird with its gentle habits and soft warbling notes is perhaps universally the best loved. The wing feathers of a bird overlap in such a way that on the up-beat air slips between them, but when the wings are brought down there are no holes or gaps for the air to get through thus providing "lift" or, as in this instance, braking power.   *See page 1136*

[10-1A]

More typical of the general colour pattern of the family, the brown and white wood thrush with its speckled breast is closely related to the European nightingales and is considered by many to be the finest songster of all American birds. The wood thrush avoids the larger cities, the Florida peninsula and northernmost New England but elsewhere in the eastern half of the United States its clear bell-like notes are quite familiar.
          See page 1136

Kinglets, gnatcatchers and Old World warblers comprise an extensive and important family of Old World song birds which has very few representatives in the Americas. One of these, the golden-crowned kinglet, is a tiny bird which is found as far north as there are trees. It nests in the northern extreme of its range, wintering throughout the United States and as far south as Mexico and Guatemala.   *See page 1140*

[10-2]

[10-2A]

The friendly, inquisitive little black-capped chickadee is a non-migratory North American bird which can easily be coaxed into the hand with sunflower seeds or peanuts, although its primary diet is small insects. Its Old World counterpart, the willowtit, was the inspiration for the well-known Gilbert and Sullivan song in "The Mikado". Some African species of this group weave their nests so skilfully that the finished product resembles heavy felt. *See page 1141*

[10-2B]

The name "nuthatch" refers to this bird's habit of jamming a nut into a crevice and then cracking it with hatchet-like blows of its strong, pointed beak. The white breasted nuthatch, the most common variety in the United States, has all the distinctive characteristics of the world-wide family. Feeding mainly on insects these birds, using only their feet to cling to the bark, will walk headfirst down a tree as casually as in the more conventional directions.   *See page 1142* prevent overcrowding, thus ensuring an ample food supply for the young.

The Cardinal, *Richmondena cardinalis,* belongs to a group of finches best represented in South America. The handsomely crested male is bright red, including even the bill; the female is much duller in colour. Though commonest in the southern United States, the cardinal is

LOVED FOR ITS BRIGHT COLOUR AND CHEERY WHISTLE

The cardinal is named for its striking red colour, which extends to its bill and distinctive crest. The bird builds its nest in a small tree or a thicket, and here it lays its three or four eggs. Feeding mainly on seeds and insects, the cardinal does considerably more good than harm. In bad winters it often relies on bird feeding stations in order to survive.

seen locally as far as New York. It does not migrate, and a severe winter in the northern part of its range plays havoc with it.

The Evening Grosbeak, *Hesperiphona vespertina,* judging from its common and scientific names, ought to be active in the evening.

EAL / 10—C

However, field observation does not bear this out to any appreciable extent. A large yellowish finch with black and white wings, it has a huge whitish bill—at least that part of its common name is accurate. It was formerly very rare in the north-east of America but now occurs there more commonly. In the West it breeds south in the mountains to Arizona, but in the East it is seen chiefly in wintertime.

The Rose-breasted Grosbeak, *Pheucticus ludovicianus,* is a handsome bird of almost robin size. One of the gems of the family, the male is black and white, with a beautiful rose-coloured throat and breast. The female is discreetly attired in grey, brown, and white. The song of the rose-breasted grosbeak, similar to the American robin's but more melodious, is uttered from the shady crown of a maple or other large tree. This grosbeak constructs a rather flimsy, cuplike nest made of rootlets, in which it lays three or four spotted eggs. In the western states we find a closely related but less striking bird, the Black-headed Grosbeak, *Pheucticus melanocephalus.*

WEAVERBIRDS—MASTER BUILDERS

Weaverbirds have a heavy bill which they use to crush seeds. At first glance this beak appears unsuitable for nest building. The fact is, though, that weaverbirds, as you can gather from their name, weave expertly constructed hanging nests. One group actually makes a nest with a spoutlike entrance at both the front and the back. These sociable birds usually nest in colonies. Some of them are very beautiful and are favourites with cage-bird fanciers. The weaverbirds comprise the family Ploceidae. Most of the 260 species of this exclusively Old World family make their home in the tropics.

Although, as we have just seen, most weaverbirds have a well-deserved reputation for first-rate nest building, a few species belonging to the genus *Viduao* are the exception that "proves" the rule. They have a lazy habit of laying their eggs in the nests of other weaverbirds and leaving it to them to hatch out the eggs and rear the young.

The House Sparrow or English Sparrow, *Passer domesticus,* is the most famous member of the weaverbird family. This is unfortunate, for this noisy, quarrelsome pest is a far from typical weaverbird. Its nest is an untidy affair, usually placed in a crevice of a building but sometimes among the branches of a tree.

House sparrows are very aggressive and bullying birds—often driving away martins and other desirable birds that favour similar places for their nest. The sparrow lays four to six spotted eggs, and brood follows brood during the warmer months of the year. Even a mild spell in winter is enough to start the males at their noisy courtship antics,

MORE TAIL THAN BIRD

The large weaverbird family includes some of the ablest nest-builders. However, the paradise whydah (*a male is shown above*) is a notable exception. The female, who is plainly coloured and lacks the long tail of her mate, lays her eggs in other whydah birds' nests, such as the one pictured. Paradise whydahs are popular cage birds.

hopping about with wings drooping and tail widely spread as they chirp with all their might. Sometimes the hen sparrow appears annoyed at this vain performance, chasing the male away or even seizing him by the bill.

The house sparrow was unwisely introduced into New York about 1850; it is now found throughout the United States and in much of Canada and Mexico. Its native home is in Europe and Asia. This sparrow's association with horses is well known, and in recent years these birds have become less abundant now that cars and tractors have so largely replaced horses. When in good plumage, the male sparrow with his black bib and chestnut marks is rather attractive. City sparrows soon become so begrimed with dirt and soot that we can no longer make out their true appearance.

The Sociable Weaver, *Philetaerus socius*, is a relative of the house sparrow. Its fabulous building activities are confined to the arid plains of southern Africa, where the traveller sometimes sees a huge mass of straw and grass about ten feet high and six or eight feet in diameter, built among the thorny branches of an acacia tree. This is the "apartment house" nest of the sociable weaver. These birds assemble in a colony of thirty pairs—or even more—and pool their efforts in building this huge structure; each pair is provided with an individual nesting chamber.

WAXBILLS AND THEIR RELATIVES

The waxbills often have exquisite colours. The Lady Gould's Finch, for example, is lilac and pink with a pointed tail; it looks like a miniature pheasant! We find some waxbills in Africa, but they have their greatest development in the Australian region. These birds belong to the subfamily Estrildinae.

The Parrot-bills, *Erythrura*, are red, blue, and green, the exact pattern varying from species to species. This is the only widespread group of weavers in the Polynesian islands—it occurs as far east as Fiji. The Ricebird, *Padda oryzivora* ("rice eater"), a grey and black species with white cheeks, is a favourite cage bird in the Philippines. Native vendors often trudge through the streets of Manila offering a pair of ricebirds in a tiny bamboo cage.

OTHER WEAVERBIRDS

There are many typical weaverbirds in the genus *Ploceus*. Best represented in Africa, they are also found in Asia. Nesting in large colonies, they hang their flasklike nests from the branches of trees or from papyrus or other tall grass. The male does most of the weaving,

and the female is content to add the nest lining. Most of these birds
have considerable yellow in their plumage, often with a black throat
or other black marks on the head. The females are more dully coloured
than their mates.

STARLINGS—ATTRACTIVE BUT AGGRESSIVE

The scientific name *vulgaris*, in the modern rather than classical
meaning of the word, fits the starling very well. Though this bird can
utter pleasant ringing whistles, it is more apt to draw attention to
itself by harsh, unpleasant, sputtering scolding—especially when an
intruder approaches its nest. This nest, by the way, is an untidy mass
of straw placed in a hole in a tree, a birdhouse, or in cornices of
buildings.

An attractive bird with its glossy, iridescent black plumage, the
starling is unfortunately much too aggressive. In the United States
the villain of the piece is the introduced Common Starling, *Sturnus
vulgaris*, the only starling of western Europe. Once domiciled in the
United States, the common starling thrived all too well, and has now
reached the Pacific coast. Very pugnacious towards native birds, such
as the flicker and the bluebird, it often kills them in their nesting
holes with a blow of its sharp bill and then pre-empts their nests. Nor
does the starling endear itself to the farmer by its occasionally destructive feeding habits; particularly annoying is its fondness for small
fruits.

Of the hundred or so species that make up the starling tribe (family
Sturnidae), all but a few dwell exclusively in the Old World tropics.
Starlings are more or less migratory, especially in the Old World,
but vast hordes of them winter in the northern cities of the United
States. Each night they throng to favoured roosts on public buildings or on the superstructure of bridges. If the neighbouring area
is illuminated to any extent by electric lights, the cries of the birds
go on all night. The starling is in fact the prime example of the folly
of introducing a foreign animal into a new country without carefully
pondering the likely results.

In the tropics, the Common Mynah, *Acridotheres tristis*, of India,
takes the place of the common starling. Like that nuisance it has
been foolishly introduced into many other localities from South Africa
to Hawaii. During the pairing or territorial squabbles of this mynah,

two or more birds often become embroiled in a bitter battle on the ground. At such times they are so engrossed in their squabbling that an alert cat may dash in and snatch one of them away.

The mynah is a typical starling: noisy, aggressive, and with slovenly nesting habits. Usually it nests in hollows like other starlings, though occasionally it builds domed nests in trees. In Hawaii the crown of a Royal Palm tree often shelters its nest.

Several kinds of starlings make interesting pets. Best known for this purpose is the Talking Mynah, *Gracula religiosa*, a native of the

A STARLING THAT TALKS

The talking mynah, a large starling of India, talks as well as a parrot or crow and makes an amusing pet. A handsome bird, the talking mynah has shiny black plumage relieved by white wing patches.

Indian region. As you can gather from its name, it learns to speak, and speaks as well as a parrot or crow. Two or even three times the size of a common starling, this bird has glossy black plumage with white patches in the wings. As is the case with many other starlings, its head is partly devoid of feathers and is ornamented with skin lappets or wattles.

The African glossy starlings are rather primitive members of the family. Some of them, like the Violet-backed Starling, *Cinnyricinclus leucogaster*, and the Long-tailed Spreo, *Spreo regius*, are very brilliant.

Though much plainer in appearance, the African Oxbirds, *Buphagus*, lead a very curious existence. These specialized starlings have the bill modified for shearing ticks from the backs of rhinos, buffaloes, and other large mammals, and feed on little else but these ticks. On the island of Celebes in the East Indies we find a species which is superficially similar though unrelated to these tick-eaters. The Celebes bird uses its strong bill to dig out nesting chambers in dead trees— behaviour that reminds us of some mynahs that dig nesting burrows in river banks.

The Rosy Pastor, *Sturnus roseus*, a more colourful relative of the common starling, nests north of India and migrates to that country to spend the winter. Every now and then there are mass movements of these birds into Europe, as far west as Hungary or even Switzerland. Making no effort to return, these birds attempt to nest in their new surroundings.

The only starlings to reach Australia and the Polynesian islands belong to the genus *Aplonis*. These plain, black birds are noteworthy because a few species nest in colonies and build long swinging nests similar to the ones made by the weaver-finches—a group to which the starlings may be related.

DRONGOS

Drongos are interesting birds. They all have a strongly hooked bill wreathed with highly developed bristles around the gape of the mouth which help them to scoop up their flying prey—insects. Drongos have a habit of sitting quietly for long periods in middle portions of deep forest. They sally out from selected perches in quest of winged insects —a trait that reminds us of large flycatchers. Often drongos accompany troops of monkeys, probably to secure insects disturbed into flight by the noisy animals. Like the American kingbird, the drongo puts up a spirited defence of its territory, even to the point of attacking hawks and crows. That is why drongos are known as "king crows" in India.

In appearance, drongos remind us of fork-tailed grackles or slender blackbirds. They are basically glossy black with bluish-green reflections. Male and female are similar in colour and size. As a rule the voice of the drongo is soft and melodious, but sometimes it produces surprising sounds—as when it mimics crows or other birds. The

thirty-odd species of drongos—they make up the family Dicruridae
—range from Africa, through Indo-Malaya to Australia. Nearly all
make their home in tropical environs, though a few are found at altitudes
up to five thousand feet in the subtropics.

THE DRONGO—A BIRD OF VARYING MOODS

The drongo is a trim-looking tropical bird which deftly catches insects on the wing. Its
pugnacity towards hawks has given it the name of "king crow" in India. Shown here is
the racket-tailed drongo. This bird is noted for its great skill as a mimic.

The typical drongo nest is a cup formed of grass, hair, or lichens,
woven securely into a low tree-crotch in deep forest. Drongos lay three
or four whitish or buff eggs with grey blotches.

WAXWINGS AND THEIR KIN

The family name of these birds, Bombycillidae, means "little silky
ones", and refers to the soft, silky texture of their plumage. Waxwings are songless, uttering only reedy, lisping notes. They feed on
fruit. Sometimes a row of them will pass a cherry or other small fruit
from one bird to another until one of them finally swallows it.

There are three species of waxwings—the Japanese Waxwing, the

Cedar Waxwing of North America, and the Bohemian Waxwing. The Bohemian variety, despite its name, lives in the colder regions of both America and Eurasia. The waxwing has a modest but pleasing colour scheme—soft browns set off by yellow-tipped tail feathers and bright red waxlike appendages on the wing feathers. The head is handsomely crested. The nest of the waxwing is a simple, open cup. This bird lays three to five mottled grey and brown eggs.

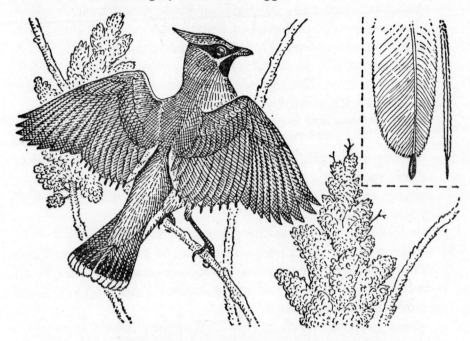

THE WAXWING—NOTED FOR ITS SILKY PLUMAGE

Though not much of a singer, the waxwing is an attractive bird, with pleasantly subdued colours, remarkably silky plumage, and a striking crest. Waxwings are mostly fruit-eaters, and a group of them will sometimes pass a cherry from bird to bird until the titbit is finally disposed of. Two views of a wax-tipped feather are shown in the detail.

The waxwing will eat insects as well as fruit. The cedar waxwing has a great appetite for cankerworms, and a single flock of waxwings may consume close to three thousand worms in a day—or so runs a recent estimate. In this way the birds make up for the damage they do to fruits.

Related to the waxwings are the Silky Flycatchers, with half a dozen species ranging from south-western United States to Panama. The best known is the Mexican "Flycatcher" or Phainopepla, a handsome black and white bird of the south-western deserts. In the winter it lives mostly on mistletoe berries. The Palm Chat, *Dulus*, which dwells on the island of Hispaniola in the West Indies, is another relative of the waxwings. Several pairs co-operate in building a large nest in which each pair has a separate nesting chamber.

WOOD SWALLOWS—SWALLOWS IN NAME ONLY

Alone among the vast array of perching birds, wood swallows have the peculiar powder downs found in herons and in some other birds. These powder downs consist of patches of continuously growing short whitish feathers which, in wood swallows, spring from the breast, thighs, and lower back. The tips of these plumes break up into a kind of talcum-like powder which helps keep the plumage in shape.

The wood swallow has long wings and a strong bill. It is chiefly notable for its graceful, floating flight which involves soaring and gliding, interspersed with short, swallow-like wingbeats. Naturalists know of ten species of these peculiar birds. The wood swallows—they comprise the family Artamidae—have no near relatives and no affinities with true swallows.

Usually found in open flocks by day and in tight clusters by night, wood swallows live in and about the crowns of tall trees growing in grasslands. As a rule they establish themselves near water and forage out from high limbs in search of flying insects. They may soar about for some time before returning to perch.

The wood swallows dwell in the Philippines, New Guinea, and Australia. Greyish black above and white below, they have long, pointed wings and bluish, waxy bills. Shortly before dusk a colony reassembles at favourite perches. Here they squeeze together for the night, back to back and side to side in tight knots. In Papua we found such tight-knit groups on slender limbs of eucalyptus trees in the lowlands. In the Philippines we discovered them in living and dead trees. If a colony is disturbed at dusk, the members explode outward in all directions; after dark it is difficult to flush them. At such times the knot of birds, when revealed by a flashlight beam, reminded us of a crumpled bath towel.

Male and female wood swallows are similar in size and colour. We are told that they co-operate in incubating and taking care of the nestlings. Often a group of them will place several nests—open cups of grass and weeds—in a small area.

SHRIKES, OR BUTCHERBIRDS

If you have ever seen a shrike, you may have noticed that there is something paradoxical in its appearance—its bill is the bill of a bird of prey, yet its feet lack the powerful grasping talons that we expect in such a bird. The bill with its sharp, strong hook, reminds you of a hawk or owl, and not without reason; the shrike has adopted the carnivorous habits of those birds and, following their example, it feeds upon mice, small birds, and large insects. In the winter, the shrike is a relentless enemy of sparrows.

THE SHRIKE—STRANGE BIRD OF PREY

There is no mistaking the meaning of the shrike's strong, sharp, hooked bill. Yet this creature lacks the talons we associate with a bird of prey. The shrike solves the problem of holding its victims by impaling them on pointed objects—thorns, for example.

But how, you may wonder, does the shrike come to grips with its prey if its feet are more or less like the feet of a songbird? The answer to this question explains why the shrike is called the "butcherbird". The shrike pursues its victim through thickets until the hunted creature becomes exhausted or confused. Thereupon the shrike, making use of the powerful bill, impales its prey upon a thorn or a barb in a wire fence, so that it becomes easy to dismember the victim. When food is plentiful, shrikes may kill more mice than they can eat, and the surplus is left impaled on thorns. Shrikes build a substantial open nest and lay four or five mottled greyish eggs. Just as you would expect, they are bold and aggressive when it comes to defending their nest.

The shrikes are an Old World family (Laniidae). Only two of the seventy-odd species reached North America, and one of these, the Northern Shrike, *Lanius excubitor*, is also to be found in the Old World.

About the size of a thrush, it is pale grey with darker wavy markings on the breast and with black facial patches.

The Migrant or Loggerhead Shrike, *Lanius ludovicianus*, is commonest in the southern United States. Somewhat smaller than its northern cousin, it feeds extensively on insects as well as mice. We find many related shrikes in Eurasia and Africa. The bush shrikes of Africa, unlike the others, are often beautiful, brightly coloured birds. They do not share the predatory habits of the other shrikes, and may be unrelated to them.

VANGAS—AT HOME IN MADAGASCAR

Only on the island of Madagascar do we find the dozen or so species of vangas, or vanga-shrikes, as they are sometimes called. As a rule they have rather heavy, hooked beaks resembling those of shrikes; yet it is doubtful if they are really close relatives of the shrikes. The bill varies in size and shape from species to species—a feature we can observe in many island birds. Thus, the Sicklebill, *Falculea*, has a long, curved bill; the Helmet Bird, *Euryceros*, has a very high, arched bill and was formerly placed in a separate family.

Most vangas are brown and black. Among the exceptions, the Blue Vanga is bright blue above and white below; the sicklebill, like the Hook-billed Vanga, is black above and white below. This hook-billed vanga, by the way, comes closer to the shrikes than does any other member of the vanga family (Vangidae).

Vangas move through the forest in mixed flocks that include birds of other families. They feed chiefly on insects, but the jay-sized sicklebill seems to favour small lizards. Vangas have a repertoire of loud, rather unmusical calls and whistles. The vanga uses leaf stems and grass for its open, cup-shaped nest, and lays two or three spotted eggs.

AUSTRALIAN BUTCHERBIRDS AND BELL MAGPIES

Like the shrikes or butcherbirds of other parts of the world, the Australian Butcherbird, *Cracticus*, kills mice, large insects, and even small birds, and impales them upon thorns while tearing them apart with its strong, hooked beak. These birds have a very large head, and a correspondingly large bill. Some are black and white, others entirely black; in size they approximate the familiar blue jay. The family has a dozen or so species, all of them making their home in the Australian region.

The Australian "Magpies", *Gymnorhina*, build a substantial nest of sticks and grass. They usually place this structure in a tree, but occasionally they locate the nest among the wires on a telegraph pole, where it has been known to cause a short circuit! The Australian "magpies" are stocky, black and white birds about the size of a small crow. They too have a hooked beak, but feed mainly on large insects they catch on the ground. These birds, with their loud, flutelike voices, are considered by some the best feathered songsters in Australia. Bold, aggressive birds, like the rest of the family, they are particularly truculent at nesting time, often attacking anyone who approaches the nest. They seem to be quite fearless on these occasions and can cause actual damage.

The Piping Crows or Currawongs, *Strepera*, are the largest members of this family (Cracticidae). The name "currawong" is an imitation of their loud notes. They are fond of fruit and often destructive about orchards. Most currawongs have white patches in the wings or tail, but some of them are almost entirely black, reminding us very much of crows.

ORIOLES—YELLOW AND ORANGE

There are orioles in America, but the "true" orioles—those of the family Oriolidae—are an Old World family of brightly coloured, mainly yellow and orange birds. Some of the more abundant and more colourful of the thirty-two species like to perch on high limbs about farmlands and in semi-open rolling country. It frequently happens that they are the most obvious and familiar birds of the landscape, especially since they are often seen in flocks. However, some orioles are very shy, preferring to dwell in the cloistered seclusion of the thick canopy of tropical and subtropical jungle.

As we have indicated, these orioles are not at all related to the American orioles. This Old World group dwells in Africa, Eurasia, Indo-Malaya, Australia, and on islands of the Western Pacific. The birds have long wings, rather weak legs and feet, and a prominent bill. Their flying is strong, direct, and heavy. Orioles have a clear, melodious call, though sometimes they resort to a rasping note of warning. They feed on fruit and insects.

Female orioles follow the familiar pattern of being far less brilliantly coloured than the males. The Black-naped Oriole, *Oriolus chinensis*, is an interesting case in point. The adult male has a golden body, while the female and young are strongly tinted with green. The best-known member of the family is perhaps the Golden Oriole of Europe, *Oriolus oriolus*, with its golden-yellow body and black wings. The Isabella Oriole, *Oriolus isabellinus*, and the White-lored Oriole, *Oriolus albilorus*, are typical of the species that dwell in the Philippine mountain forests. Both are small yellowish birds with olive markings; they are very little known because of their elusive habits.

CROWS AND JAYS—CLEVEREST OF BIRDS

Crows and ravens are able to maintain their numbers in many places where every man's hand is against them. Indeed, many naturalists consider these resourceful birds the most highly evolved and the cleverest of all feathered creatures. Crows and ravens, the largest members of the family Corvidae, have entered many parts of the world—Australia and the Hawaiian Islands, for example—where other birds of the family, such as jays and magpies, have failed to gain a foothold.

You have probably heard of the ability of some tame crows to learn to speak a few words. There is a popular belief that you have to split a crow's tongue before it can talk, but this notion is false. Crows are mischievous birds, fond of pranks, and they make amusing pets. They have been known to pull clothes pegs off washing lines. Bright objects have an irresistible attraction for them, and they sometimes hide away metal and glass objects. They are given to breaking up the nests of small birds, and their fondness for corn and farmyard eggs makes them the farmer's traditional enemy. However, they eat a good many insects, as well as small mice, rats, and young rabbits. The crow has a sizable wingspread—about three feet—and is a splendid flier. It flies in a straight line—hence the proverbial expression, "as the crow flies".

The American Crow, *Corvus brachyrhynchos*, is a common bird throughout most of America. During spring and summer it scatters in pairs or small groups over the country, but in winter—it is not much of a migrator—immense numbers congregate each night to roost. By day they spread to a distance of twenty or thirty miles from the roost to glean any edible matter, vegetable or animal, that they can find. The crow is a very shy and suspicious bird and, apart from man, has few enemies. The great horned owl sometime seizes a roosting crow at night and is, in turn, unmercifully mobbed by frantic flocks of crows whenever they find its daytime retreat.

RAVENS AND ROOKS

The Raven, *Corvus corax*, is found throughout the Northern Hemisphere. Famous for its jet plumes and dismal croaking, this bird was symbolic of ill fortune and death long before Edgar Allan Poe wrote

THE RAVEN—INTELLIGENT AND ADAPTABLE

Noted for its ingenuity when it comes to obtaining food, the raven is also remarkably adaptable to a variety of conditions. It is equally at home in deserts, high mountains, or the Arctic region, and is a destroyer of rodents and insects on a large scale. Captive birds show intelligence and may learn to speak a bit, but are mischievous.

The Raven. A bird of the wilderness, unlike the crow, it is commonest in the deserts and mountains of the American West; in the East we find it locally in the highest Appalachians south to North Carolina.

The raven is among the most adaptable of birds. Some ravens dwell in the burning deserts of the South-west, others are among the few birds capable of spending the winter in Greenland. In such regions it displays an ingenuity in securing food that is nothing short of phenomenal. One raven was observed to pull the tail of an Eskimo dog to distract its attention while a second raven darted in to snatch a morsel of food momentarily ignored by the enraged husky.

Ravens have a diet which if anything is even more wide-ranging than the crows'. Sometimes ravens feed like vultures on the carcass of a dead animal.

Often they hide away surplus food in a crevice or bury it beneath leaves or a shallow layer of soil. This is characteristic practice of the hundred or so members of the family. Apart from the well-known croak, ravens sometimes utter a gurgling sound, like water coming out of a jug, when they soar to a great height.

The Rook, *Corvus frugilegus*, is the most familiar bird of the crow tribe in England. A colony of a thousand birds may nest in a grove. If they see a man with a gun, they fly off their nests with much cawing. Once a year, during the nesting season, a "rook shoot" is organized to keep their numbers within reasonable bounds.

JAYS—BOLD AND JAUNTY

The Blue Jay, *Cyanocitta cristata*, has a conspicuous crest and attractive blue and white plumage. This jaunty-looking bird is common throughout the eastern United States. In parts of the West it is replaced by its cousin the Steller's Jay, which has more uniform, darker-bluish plumage.

Blue jays are bold creatures, as you can tell when you hear their noisy screams as they roam through the trees in search of food. Always ready to mob a sleepy owl or to follow and torment a fox, they eat almost anything—insects, grain, fruit, and acorns. In the spring they add the eggs and young of small birds to their bill of fare. Although some blue jays migrate, their unusually extensive diet makes it possible for many of them to winter in the north. Against a landscape of snow and evergreens they are especially handsome.

Both male and female take part in building the nest and feeding

The exclusively American family of vireos is made up of some 40 species with a remarkable uniformity of habits in spite of the great disparity in their choice of environment. They are at home from sea-level to altitudes of 9,000 feet, the species that breed in the colder regions of the Northern Hemisphere migrating to the tropics in winter. The red-eyed vireo, found anywhere there are trees in number, is the most familiar and widespread species.   *See page 1148*

[10-3]

[10-3A]

The Baltimore oriole gets its name from its orange and black colouring—the colours of the House of Baltimore, founders of Maryland. While the female is not as brightly hued as the male, she still shows enough orange to be recognized easily. This is the only species of orioles common in the northern United States; a few varieties are found in the west and southwest, but for the most part the orioles are native to the American tropics. (The "true" orioles are an Old World family of brightly coloured orange or yellow birds.) The deep nest carefully woven of grass, horsehair and odd bits of string, is typical of the family; nests of the tropical oropendolas may be three feet long.   *See page 1153*

The spectacular, unmistakable red-winged blackbird with his brilliant scarlet shoulder patches on an otherwise glossy black body is one of the ten most abundant birds of the United States. The females, a dusky brown with a heavily streaked breast, lack the shoulder markings. Originally marsh birds, the redwings have learned to make their nests in dry hayfields. *See page 1150*

[10-4]

[10-4A]

The male and female meadowlark are very similar in size and coloration. The two most familiar American species so resemble each other it is difficult to tell them apart, although the western variety is slightly paler in colour than the eastern and has a more melodious song. Like quail, meadowlarks have a chunky build and fly in alternating rapid bursts of wingbeats and short glides; as a consequence they are often shot as game birds. *See page 1149*

[10-4B]

Closely related to the blackbirds, meadowlarks and orioles, the grackles in general have very little to recommend them. Both the male and female of the bronzed grackle are black but the male's feathers are highly iridescent, showing various metallic hues in sunlight—a characteristic shared by male grackles of all species. Slightly modified variations of this jay-sized bird with its "rusty gate" voice are found throughout the United States and Mexico.

See page 1151

THE APTLY NAMED
BIRD OF PARADISE

A throat of brilliant shining green, a breast of resplendent purple, and beautiful rosy-orange back plumes make the male greater bird of paradise one of Nature's marvels. By contrast his demurely coloured mate lacks all the bright colours and the ornamental plumes. See page 1180.

HE DISPLAYS HIS SPLENDOURS

Suddenly impelled to give his courtship display, the colourful bird of paradise throws his filmy plumes in a shimmering mass above his back. At the same time, with bill widely agape, he utters a series of challenging calls. See page 1180.

Bird of Paradise photos:
New York Zoological Society

THE CLIMAX OF A WONDERFUL DANCE

Still more frenzied, he inclines his body far forward, displaying the rosy-orange plumes and widespread wings to his mate. The impression is a vivid one, even as viewed here in black and white.

the young, but only the female incubates the eggs. This is generally true of all the birds of this family. While the female blue jay is incubating the eggs, she is sometimes fed by her mate. The substantial nest is built of sticks, lined with finer materials, and the four or five eggs are mottled with grey and brown. Blue jays hide their nest carefully, and they are quiet and furtive in its vicinity unless danger threatens —then they sometimes launch a courageous counter-attack.

In the South-west, the best-known jay is the Scrub Jay or California Jay, *Cyanocitta coerulescens*. Though lacking the blue jay's crest, it is rather similar in habits and even more partial to the eggs of other birds. The Florida Jay, an exceptionally fearless and inquisitive bird found locally in Florida, is an eastern form of the scrub jay.

Clark's Nutcracker, *Nucifraga columbiana*, is a black and white bird you can see only if you visit the Rocky Mountains. It has a harsh, grating call that can be heard for quite a distance. As you can gather from its name, this bird cracks nuts with its heavy, pointed bill. The nutcracker nests high in the mountains early in the spring when the ground is still covered with several feet of snow. It builds a very thick walled nest and lines it warmly with fur and feathers.

MAGPIES

The colourful, long-tailed magpies are best represented in the Orient, but the Common Magpie, *Pica pica*, has entered North America by way of Siberia and Alaska and is common in the arid western parts of the continent. A handsome bird of white and shining bluish-black plumage, it has a partiality for young birds, including poultry and game birds, that does not endear it to the rancher. The magpie builds a large domed structure with a side entrance, lining the walls with mud.

WATTLE-BIRDS—NEW ZEALAND ODDITIES

It is curious that this group of New Zealand birds contains three species that show little resemblance to each other, apart from the common feature of a small wattle on the side of the head. Particularly striking is the difference in the shape of the bill. The most remarkable of these species, the Huia, *Neomorpha acutirostris*, is now almost extinct. It is unique among birds of the world for the degree of difference between the bill of the male and the female. The male's bill is stout and only moderately curved; the female's is much longer and more slender. They make a good team—the male uses his strong bill to dig away bark and soft wood, exposing the burrows of grubs, which his mate then picks out with her slender bill.

The huia is a crow-sized black and white bird with a long tail. Like the other two species of the family Callaeidae, it has weak wings but long, powerful legs. Thus it is able to thread its way through the dense New Zealand bush by a series of long hops, sometimes aided by a flip of the wings.

The Wattled Crow, *Callaeas wilsoni*, is a greyish bird with a short, heavy bill—quite unlike the huia's. The third species, known as the Saddleback because of its chestnut-coloured back, is much smaller. Both the wattled crow and the saddleback still exist in New Zealand, though their numbers are greatly reduced.

BIRDS OF PARADISE—NEW GUINEA'S WONDER-BIRDS

It is doubtful whether the marvellous colours and bizarre ornaments of birds of paradise can be matched by any other living creature, with the possible exception of the humming-bird. The accessory plumes of these birds vary from slender bejewelled rackets and flags to feathers resembling the daintiest lace. So far as we know, the first bird of paradise to appear in Europe was brought back to Spain in 1522 by Captain El Cano, Magellan's successor on his celebrated globe-encircling voyage. He obtained this unbelievably beautiful creature on the island of Tidore in the Moluccas, where the natives called it *manukdewata* ("bird of the gods").

Soon the lovely bird inspired a series of imaginative tales—it was said to gaze perpetually into the sun, and to carry its young among the soft feathers of its back. Later the observations of naturalists made it possible to separate fact from fancy. Yet we have here the kind of subject where fancy pales before fact. For centuries people believed that these exquisite birds were wanderers from the realms of heaven itself. The legless state of the early skins that filtered into Europe was partly responsible for this myth; above all, these birds came from the unknown and were truly of unearthly beauty. Yet, once the "prosaic" naturalists got to work, they discovered a fact which is more fantastic than all these myths: the bird of paradise is a resplendent relative of that sombre bird, the crow!

Until recently, bird of paradise plumes were prized by milliners; no woman, whether princess or cabaret queen, considered a wardrobe complete if it lacked these plumes. So insistent was the demand that collectors poured into the forbidding and often deadly jungles of New Guinea—the principal home of the birds of paradise—to reap a harvest of skins which, in the peak year of 1910, totalled one hundred thousand male birds.

As the relentless hunt went on, many of the forty-two species of birds of paradise (family Paradisaeidae) began to disappear, and conservationists the world over feared for their survival. Fortunately, at long last laws were passed that served to halt the feather traffic before any permanent loss was inflicted. This was the end of a trade which, so history tells us, was started more than five hundred years ago. A curious sidelight of this laudable legislation is that many New Guinea settlements became virtual ghost towns and the economy of the island was seriously shaken.

The old plume-hunting days seem to be forgotten today. There is very little poaching. Even during the Second World War, when thousands of soldiers bivouacked for extended periods amid the very trees in which birds of paradise flourished, very few of these beautiful creatures were seen, let alone killed. The native tribes are permitted to kill all they wish for dance decorations and the like, and they extract quite a toll in the highlands where plumes are still more valuable than gold in the native economy. Other than these and the few taken by occasional scientific collectors, no birds are killed; most of the species are now flourishing.

HOW THE BIRDS LIVE

Birds of paradise feed on fruit, berries, seeds, and insects taken from a wide variety of forest habitats. These may be at sea-level, or they may be at an altitude of twelve thousand feet in the mountains. The Yellow-wattled Bird of Paradise, *Macgregoria*, lives in the sub-alpine forest that begins at about ten thousand feet. Some birds of paradise are equipped to pick food from bark surfaces, or to dig in rotten wood to which they cling like woodpeckers; others probe in wet moss in the cloud forest for insects, and still others feed on insects from flowering trees of the forest canopy.

Some birds of paradise are as small as thrushes, others are the size of a small crow, but with very long tail plumes. A few are surprisingly

rather sombre in colour, with the male resembling the female; this is
true of a group known as the manucodes. The fact that the males help
their mates with the nesting duties is another indication that the manucodes are a primitive group.

THE PLUME BIRDS

However, we are naturally more interested in the brighter-coloured
birds of paradise—the plume birds. Among all these the males have
elaborate courtship displays, given usually on jealously defended tree
locations but sometimes on the ground. The females are attracted
only briefly to the males and then build a nest and raise a family entirely
unassisted. The nests are loosely constructed, though sometimes they
may be bulky, open cups placed at varying elevations up to ninety feet.
The eggs are notable for the streaklike brown markings that run almost
from one end of the egg to the other.

FAMOUS BIRDS OF PARADISE

Among the more typical birds of paradise, the male is excessively
ornamented with plumes and often brilliantly coloured as well. The
female is sombre in colour, and she lacks accessory plumage. We see
this well exemplified in the great tailed birds of paradise, *Astrapia*
and *Epimachus*; the dark-coloured, highly iridescent males have lengthy
tail feathers which are sometimes black, sometimes nearly pure white,
while the females are short-tailed, brownish creatures.

The Sickle-billed Bird of Paradise, *Epimachus meyeri*, dwells in high
mountain forests. The male is a dark-greyish bird with lacy flank
plumes, a long, curved bill, a massive, glossy-edged chest-shield, and
a long spearlike tail. The female is maroon above and grey-barred
below.

When we come to the fabled Ribbon-tailed Bird of Paradise, a
glittering, green-headed black bird known only from the highlands
of Mt. Hagen, we find that the tail of the adult male reaches a length
of thirty-nine inches—or more than five times the length of the body!
A curious feature of these birds is that in adult males the tail is pure
white with narrow black tips, while in the immature male the tail
has the black tips sometimes extending over a third of its length.
Younger birds have variable amounts of white, or none at all—a
factor which has led to much confusion; in the black stage, they

closely resemble the immature Princess Stephanie Bird of Paradise, *Astrapia stephaniae*, which dwells at similar altitudes. The two hybridize freely.

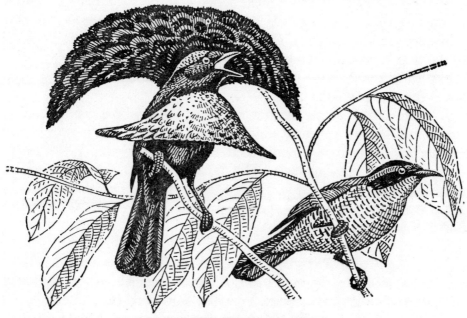

THE SUPERB BIRD OF PARADISE

This magnificent bird has a large cape of specialized feathers which covers its entire back. On its breast it has a shield glowing with a metallic lustre like a brilliant medallion. To attract a mate, the male perches on an exposed tree limb and utters rasping notes. He then makes his display, erecting the cape like an Indian headdress and opening wide his mouth, which is aqua green within.

The Greater Bird of Paradise, *Paradisaea apoda*, is perhaps the best-known member of the family. Its scientific name means "bird of paradise without feet" because the first trade skins brought to Europe had had the feet removed. We were fortunate enough to observe these birds in southern New Guinea in 1948; we found them travelling in bands through the upper tier of the virgin forest from near sea level to altitudes of five thousand feet.

The male is jay-sized, but because of his greatly elongated flame-coloured plumes, he appeared as large as a crow. The head is straw yellow, the forehead and throat gleaming green, and the chest deep maroon. The female is rather similar in size, drab brown, and she lacks the plumes. Morning and evening, bands of these birds travel through the forest on regular routes to favoured dancing trees on the

forest edge or on the crests of small ridges. There a male displays
on a previously selected stage which he defends against other males
who congregate to watch from the sides. They flap their wings together
over the back as they hop, all the while keeping up a raucous chorus
of crowlike and guttural calls and appearing resplendent in the rays
of the rising or setting sun. The purpose, of course, is to attract females
to the tree. Females—of which there is always a large following—select
a resplendent mate with the same noisy deliberation that some house-
wives select a new hat.

A professional plume hunter of other days whom we visited in
Papua said he had collected nine hundred males of this very common
lowland species in 1908. He sold them to a Dutch trader at Port Moresby
for one pound sterling each. The bulk of 28,300 skins of birds of
paradise, which made up a single shipment to a British concern in
1912, was doubtless of this species; yet even such wholesale slaughter
failed to have any lasting effect.

The Blue Bird of Paradise, *Paradisaea rudolphi*, a rare and beautiful
bird, lives higher in the mountains. Skins of the male of this bird sold
for twenty-five pounds apiece in 1908, but very few, if any, were
offered for sale. Their high price was due not only to their beauty but
to the inaccessibility of the country where they lived.

This bird has a velvety black body, the bill and eye-ring are white,
and the wings and tail are opalescent blue. The flank and abdomen
plumes are gorgeously tinted with lavender, purple, and blue, and
have the texture of delicate lace. The abdomen is streaked with maroon.
Black plumes, two feet long, each tipped with a jewel-like spot of opal,
spring in great fixed curves from the base of the tail. The brownish
female is plumeless and has blue wings.

We were lucky to find a ridge of rain forest high in the Owen Stanley
Mountains which was thickly populated with these magnificent birds.
In little jungle clearings solitary females were found perching twenty
to forty feet up and usually several hundred yards apart. Throughout
the day they emitted a rasping, explosive call apparently answering
a male that occasionally called "co-lee, co-lee" from high overhead.
Like several others of the richly plumed birds, this species displays
from a pendulous position, hanging straight down from the perch
and thus permitting the fanlike plumes to open up to their fullest
splendour.

The Twelve-wired Bird of Paradise, *Seleucides ignotus*, another famous bird, lives in lowland sago swamps. As you can gather from the name, the male has twelve wirelike spines, each about a foot long and sharply bent, which spring from the tips of the fragile lemon-yellow flank plumes. Except for the iridescent purple wings, the body is greenish velvety black, brighter on the back. On the chest there is a blackish shield forming an oval background in which the head may be centred and displayed. Curiously enough, the inside of the mouth in the male is greenish cobalt blue and the iris of the eye is scarlet, while in the female these parts are pale yellow. A twelve-wired bird of paradise lived for more than twenty years in the New York Zoological Park.

The Six-wired Bird of Paradise or Flagbird, *Parotia lawesi*, is an incredible creature. One, which we collected in the high mountains of Papua, was velvety black above with bluish-green reflections on the crown, whitish tips on the forehead and chin, metallic green on the throat, sides of the face, and chest, and with a distensible hooplike skirt of long feathers springing from the lower chest. When erected, this dress almost encircled the bird and concealed all of the body and legs below the chest. This species cleans a small bit of jungle floor and this it uses for its display and mating dance.

MacGregor's Bird of Paradise, *Cnemophilus macgregorii*, to date encountered exclusively in the highlands of New Guinea, is every bit as bizarre and highly pigmented as the cock-of-the-rock of South America. It is bright gold, heavily washed with scarlet. Its crown is adorned with six curious plumes projecting upward from the base of the bill. We have taken this strange bird from the forest crown at altitudes between 7,500 and 11,000 feet. Until a short while ago, the creature was generally supposed to be one of the bowerbird family.

The King of Saxony Bird of Paradise, *Pteridophora alberti*, is the most amazing member of this fascinating family. It has two tremendously long wirelike plumes springing from the sides of the crown. Each is decorated with thirty-five or so waxy flags, all growing like giant saw-teeth from one side of the shaft. Sky-blue in colour, they have an enamel-like surface. The bird itself is something of an anticlimax, being rather like a thrush. It is velvety black above and on the throat, with a pronounced shoulder cape and a vivid egg-yolk-yellow abdomen.

What use the King of Saxony made of its bizarre plumes remained a mystery until very recently. We had the good fortune to discover this exceedingly rare bird on its home grounds in the central highlands of New Guinea in 1950 and to study and photograph the courtship dance of the male.

The King of Saxony bird of paradise displays on a thin limb tip forty to seventy feet up in a primeval sentinel tree in thick forest. In mountains bordering the Wahgi Valley we found such perches at altitudes from 7,300 to 8,500 feet. The display consists of rapid dancing and graceful bowing toward the female. She is apparently first drawn to the dance arena by an intermittently delivered, explosive, hisslike call. As the male undulates rapidly, his plumes arched and quivering over his back, he slowly bows to the female. She approaches nervously to within a foot and a half of the resplendent male. In bowing, the enormous head quills slowly sweep forward over the lowered head until they protrude menacingly like the horns of an infuriated bull. (This comparison may seem out of place in describing the bird of paradise, but it suggests itself irresistibly to the observer.) Following several more bows, the birds reach their highest pitch of excitement; the male again delivers his explosive call, at the same time leaping freely upward about eighteen inches and then flying off with the female.

BOWERBIRDS—GREATEST BUILDERS OF THEM ALL

Relatives of the birds of paradise, bowerbirds are noted above all for their building of bowers. These structures are basically places where the males display to attract mates; but building bowers is so ingrained that the birds apparently devote much time to it, even during the seasons when they are not nesting. They place the true nests some distance away from the bowers; these nests are not remarkable in any way.

SOME ARE BRIGHTLY COLOURED

Bowerbirds do not have the ornamental plumes of the birds of paradise, but some of them are brightly coloured. Thus, the male Regent Bird, *Sericulus*, has a pattern of rich orange yellow and black.

The male Satin Bowerbird, *Ptilonorhynchus*, is deep blue through-out; even his eyes are blue and kept wide open and bulging when he is displaying to his mate. A few members of the family Ptilono-rhynchidae lack bright colours altogether. Eight species of bowerbirds dwell in Australia and about an equal number in New Guinea.

OUTSTANDING BUILDERS

The builder of the most elaborate bowers is the Golden Bowerbird, *Prionodura newtonia*. A typical bower consists of an archway or bridge built of interlaced vines and stems. Its walls are ornamented with berries, ferns, and mosses. Two piles of sticks, one at either end, support the bower, which covers several square feet.

Among other species the bower is often ornamented with shells, bits of glass, or any brightly coloured object the bird can find. One species covers its display area with green leaves, picked fresh each morning. But most remarkable of all is the "painting" of the walls of its bower by the satin bowerbird. In the wild it uses black earth, ashes, or coloured soil, mixed with its own saliva and applied with a bit of frayed bark. The following account of the behaviour of one of these birds in captivity was published by Dr. Crandall, Curator of Birds at the New York Zoological Park.

"In February, 1922, a keeper called my attention to the antics of a satin bowerbird, which followed him about the aviary, nibbling at the soft wood of a sieve the man was using. I watched the bird for some time, and finally discovered that the particles of wood were 'chewed' until they had become thoroughly mixed with saliva, and that the resul-tant paste was smeared on the twigs that lined the inner walls of the bower. A piece of dry rotten wood was then placed in the cage and an orgy of plastering followed. When the deposit had become dry, we found that most of the inner twigs were well covered with a thick greyish coat of crumbling consistency."

This painting, in which, as we have noted, a bit of bark or wood is sometimes used as a "brush", is one of the very few authentic instances of the use of a tool or implement by a bird or, for that matter, by any animal below the human level. Perhaps the only other example is the use of a twig by one of the Galápagos finches, to poke out insects.

The Gardener Bowerbirds, *Amblyornis*, are better known, and justly famous. Most of them are brown and quail-sized, with enormous golden-orange crests. In 1950 we came across the bower of one of these birds, *Amblyornis macgregoriae*, in central New Guinea, nine thousand feet above sea level. The bower was constructed of twigs placed around a sapling, in deep forest, to a height of nearly four feet. The bird-architect had thus formed a slender wooden Eiffel-Tower-like structure. About its base every vestige of debris for a diameter of three feet had been cleared away and the immaculate arena thus formed was cloaked in fine-textured moss. Around this area circled a mossy wall several inches in height. We saw the attentive male flicking the massive golden crest over his head and heard him emit resonant crackling sounds and deep ventriloquial notes.

This bird lays a single pale-buff egg, in June or July, in a strong cup nest of wiry rootlets encased in dried leaf. The structure is hidden low in a small forest tree.

Sanford's Bowerbird, *Archboldia papuensis sanfordi*, dwells in the central highlands of New Guinea. It is a jay-sized black bird with a long rakish golden crest. The female is brownish black. Gilliard discovered this remarkable creature in July, 1950. Naturalists know nothing of the bird's life history, apart from the fact that it makes a dance ground of withered fern fronds in fern-clad forest at eight thousand feet or thereabouts.

The dance ground we discovered was surrounded by more than fifty empty snail shells and by piles of beetle skeletons. Several of the birds we examined had been feeding on bluish berries. Our eleven male and female captives were all trapped at the same meeting ground during a fifteen-day period.

Section III

AMPHIBIANS AND REPTILES
OF THE WORLD

———

CHARLES M. BOGERT

Amphibians, Pioneers on Land

WHERE THE AMPHIBIANS CAME FROM

AMPHIBIANS—animals that live both on land and in water—have a long past. It began ages ago, in the sea, cradle of life. Our earth, now estimated to be between two and three billion years old, was not exactly in its infancy when the first backboned animal made its way to land. This great pioneer was a fish, and it parted company with other fishes some 340 million years ago, to become the forefather of our modern frogs and salamanders.

The change from a water-dwelling animal to one that could live on land required much time. Limbs had to develop from fins, and lungs from an air bladder, which in the fish ancestor may already have been used for breathing. Indeed, the existing lungfish of Africa—a strange fish that breathes with lungs as well as gills, and can survive for months out of water—gives us an inkling of how the first amphibian acquired the ability to leave the sea. Nevertheless, all modern amphibians—scientists group them in the class Amphibia—still pass through a gilled stage, even though the offspring of a few kinds lose their gills before they come out of the egg.

There are several reasons why water is important in the lives of all amphibians. They lay their eggs either in water or in some moist place. Their skin is especially suited to their double life, being constantly moist—whereas reptiles on land have a dry, scaly skin. (There are other interesting differences between amphibians and reptiles, as we shall see later on. Reptiles lay their eggs on land; they depend on sunlight to heat their bodies; their food requirements are much smaller than those of amphibians.)

Coming back to the amphibians, we find that tiny glands in their skin produce a slimy substance: mucus. This makes it possible for the amphibian to "breathe" through its skin as well as through its gills or lungs. Indeed, some salamanders have neither gills nor lungs and breathe largely through the lining of the mouth and throat and their skin. On land, unless the surrounding air is filled with moisture, water from the mucus covering the skin evaporates, causing a toad or a salamander to be colder than the air or the ground beneath it. Amphibians get all the moisture they require through the skin, by entering the water or by simply absorbing it from wet earth; but they do not drink, nor can they absorb moisture from a humid atmosphere.

The first land-dwelling backboned animals retained the scaly body as well as some other characteristics of their fish ancestors. The fossils we have found suggest that amphibians had been on land for some time before their scales were replaced by the glandular skin that most of them now have. We know that traces of the scales of the pioneer amphibians are hidden in the skin of some of the superficially worm- or eel-like caecilians. These are strange limbless amphibians restricted to humid regions in the tropics.

With no other backboned animals on land to dispute their claims, the earliest amphibians seem to have thrived in their new environment. Their limbs became stronger, and their backbone took on the structure needed to carry the weight of a body no longer supported by the buoyancy of the water. They grew in size, without ever becoming real giants; they probably never produced anything so large as a ten-foot alligator. But for a time the amphibians were the masters of the solid earth. They reached their peak of abundance some 200 million years ago—140 million years after emerging from the sea. It was about this time that one progressive group began to develop into reptiles.

WHERE AMPHIBIANS LIVE

Amphibians did not dominate the earth for long, and most of those now in existence are relatively small. But we cannot call them an unsuccessful group, for they have managed to invade nearly all parts of the earth, except the seas and the Arctic regions. Despite their need for moisture, toads have even entered the deserts.

Nearly one-tenth of the twenty-five hundred known kinds of amphibians live within the borders of the United States. Fewer than forty are recorded for the whole of Europe, the best explored of the continents. Those in the vast tropical rain-forest areas of Africa and South America are not so well known. Such regions as the Amazon basin of South America and the Cameroons in Africa are teeming with frogs, in such numbers that it may be years before all the kinds living there are found and classified.

THE THREE GROUPS OF AMPHIBIANS

We readily separate modern amphibians into three main groups: frogs, salamanders, and caecilians. The caecilians lack a satisfactory common name because few people ever see them in the tropical regions where they live.

Frogs are the most abundant of the three and are easily recognized in the adult stage because they have no tail. (It disappears when they grow out of the tadpole stage.) On land they move by leaps and jumps. In fact, their group name *Salientia* is derived from the Latin word meaning "to leap".

Salamanders, unlike frogs, keep their youthful tail throughout their lives. In this respect they more closely resemble the earliest "fish on land". As a rule they crawl or walk on land, instead of leaping or hopping. In the water, however, salamanders propel themselves with their tail. Two species of salamanders that never venture on land have lost their hind limbs completely.

Only the caecilians have no limbs at all. Those that live in water swim like eels, with sinuous movements of their body. Others are limited to moist areas, mostly in tropical forests, where they crawl about like burrowing limbless lizards. If not examined closely, they could be mistaken for earthworms. Most caecilians are a foot or less in length; but one kind has a snakelike body five feet long.

After this brief survey of 340 million years of amphibian life, we turn to the fascinating details of amphibian existence among the two leading groups—the salamanders and related creatures, and the tail-less amphibians, the frogs and the toads.

Salamanders, Hellbenders, Newts, and Their Relatives—Amphibians with Tails

ALL SALAMANDERS have tails. This feature alone is enough to distinguish them from frogs. Many salamanders begin their existence in the water, where the female lays her eggs. Legs appear early in the life of the larva (the young, immature animal). Except for the gills, which extend on each side at the back of the head, the larva closely resembles its parents.

Larval salamanders, the young ones with gills, have true teeth. In this respect they also differ from tadpoles (larval frogs), which have a black beak and several rows of tiny horny combs to scrape off food.

Salamanders ordinarily have four toes on their front limbs and five toes on their hind ones. A few salamanders have lost some of their toes. The Mud Sirens, *Siren* and *Pseudobranchus*, of the south-eastern United States have completely lost their hind limbs. In the same general region of the United States, the great eel-like salamander known as the Congo Eel, *Amphiuma means*, has both pairs of limbs so reduced that only two toes remain.

When a toad loses a leg it is forced to spend the rest of its life without it. The salamander is better off in this respect, for it can regenerate or regrow lost limbs. The salamander can also regrow a lost tail. Only two kinds of reptiles can do this: the lizards (with some exceptions) and the lizard-like creature known as the tuatara.

Salamanders resemble frogs in having a moist skin filled with tiny glands. In some newts—*Triturus*, for example—these glands produce a poison that discourages enemies from eating the newts. Other glands give off a mucus or slime that makes the animal slippery and difficult to hold. When the salamander is on land, water is constantly being lost from this mucus through evaporation, unless the air is saturated

THE BULLFROG—OGRE OF THE LILY POND

This largest of American frogs is a menace to practically every creature that shares its pond home. It eats smaller frogs of all kinds, fish, the nymphs of dragonflies, other water insects, worms, and practically anything that fits in its huge mouth. *See page 1229.*

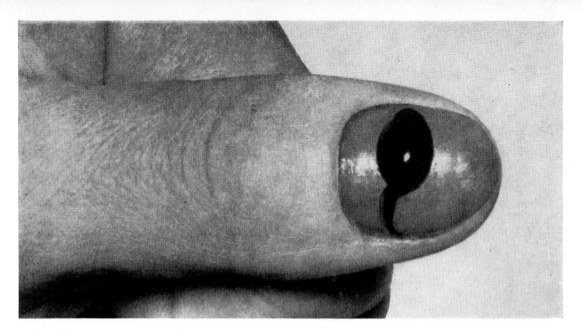

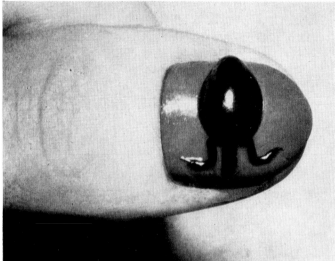

THREE STAGES IN THE GROWTH OF AN AMERICAN TOAD TADPOLE

(*Top*) The tail becomes proportionately shorter with the hind legs about to appear.

(*Centre*) The hind legs grow larger and forelimbs begin to develop beneath the skin.

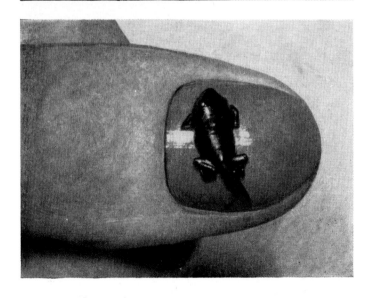

(*Bottom*) All four limbs have developed, lungs have been substituted for gills. Tadpole will soon be ready to leave the water as a toad. See page 1222.

with moisture. That is why most land-dwelling salamanders are found in regions where there is abundant rainfall. Such places as the cloud-shrouded mountains of Virginia, Tennessee, and the Carolinas are salamander havens. But even there salamanders prefer to venture forth only at night.

Salamanders, hellbenders, newts, and their relatives comprise the order Caudata (creatures with tails).

WHERE SALAMANDERS LIVE

Salamanders live in ponds, lakes, rivers, creeks, and brooks. They also dwell in underground waters and in caves, on mountains and hill-sides—even in tree cavities. But salamanders do not live in deserts, for in order to "breathe" through their skin, they need a moist atmosphere. A few amphibians live in brackish water, but there are no sea-going frogs and salamanders.

There are more kinds of salamanders in North America than in all other parts of the globe combined. Over 125 species and subspecies occur in the United States alone, and there are many more in Mexico. There are quite a few kinds in Europe and Asia, but none in Australia and only three in Africa.

Salamanders shun bright light and dry air. Except for the newts, it is unusual to find them abroad during the daylight hours. They can ordinarily be found in moist places under rocks or logs. A few live in caves, where they crawl about the walls in search of millipedes or such insects as mole crickets. In the Dixie Caverns near Salem, Virginia, Mr. Clifford H. Pope and Dr. James Fowler found the Dixie Salamander, *Plethodon wehrlei dixi*, crawling about on the stalactites in such abundance that scores of them could be seen at one time.

In Kansas, Missouri, Arkansas, and Oklahoma the Ozark Blind Salamander, *Typhlotriton spelaeus*, is so fond of caves that the adults are never found elsewhere. No light penetrates the dark inner recesses of the caverns. The salamanders' eyes, of no value under such conditions, are reduced to remnants. However, if reared in the laboratory where light is provided, they retain their eyes.

As for the larvae, they have turned up in streams outside, as well as in the underground passages. They have normal eyes and are not unlike the gilled larvae of other salamanders that begin life in the water. They mature, lose their gills, and crawl about the walls.

EAL / 10—E

Scientists believe that such salamanders retire to caves in order to escape the heat of summer. With few exceptions, notably the Newts, *Triturus*, salamanders cannot tolerate high temperatures.

IT LIVES IN DARKNESS

The adult Ozark blind salamander spends its life in pitch-dark caverns. As a result of disuse, its eyes gradually turn into mere remnants. Yet the offspring, if reared in surroundings with enough light, turn out to have normal eyes.

Salamanders, unlike snakes and lizards, prefer low body temperatures, and some kinds can remain active when scarcely above freezing. Those living in cold regions can survive being frozen within a block of ice, even though a body temperature two or three degrees *below* freezing would kill them. The Mount Lyell Salamander, *Hydromantes platycephalus*, habitually lives at high altitudes in the Sierras of California.

It is often found active in water melting from snow banks. In fact, it dies unless it is kept cold.

Because salamanders require cool surroundings, a number of species in the United States are found only in underground waters and artesian wells. Two kinds of salamanders have retreated to the cool underground waters in the southern part of the United States. With the waning of cold climates in that region, they may have been stranded in surroundings that were warmer than they could tolerate on the surface.

Glaciers never covered all of Texas as they did New England, but it may have been much colder where the Texan Blind Salamander, *Typhlomolge rathbuni*, now lives in some of the artesian wells of the Lone Star State. And the Georgian Blind Salamander, *Haideotriton wallacei*, which was discovered in the water from a deep well in Dougherty County, Georgia, may at one time have found life tolerable on the surface.

Both of these underground-water salamanders have a pale, ghostly appearance. Like the Ozark blind salamander they have only the barest remnants of eyes, well hidden below the skin. They differ from it, however, in that they never lose their gills. It is extremely doubtful whether they ever leave the water, and little is known about their breeding habits. In fact, the Georgian blind salamander was unknown until 1939 when a single specimen came into the possession of my friend and colleague, Dr. A. F. Carr, of the University of Florida. It may be years before another individual is brought up from the depths of the same well or from others in the vicinity.

HOW SALAMANDERS BREATHE

The ways of breathing of the salamander family vary greatly. While all the larvae use gills for breathing, some adults have lungs, some have gills (like fish), and some have neither, breathing only through their skin and the lining of the mouth and throat.

In addition to the underground dwellers, the Mud Puppies, *Necturus maculosus*, their close relatives, and a few other salamanders keep their larval gills into adulthood. They live in lowland streams, or even lakes, throughout most of the United States east of the Rocky Mountains, and they are sometimes well over a foot long. The main branches of their gills are covered with hairlike filaments that give them a furry appearance. Blood is carried in through tiny vessels or capillaries into each filament, where oxygen from the water enters the blood. Waste matter leaves through the same filaments. Salamanders living in stagnant pools where there is little oxygen in the water, tend to have more elaborate gills than those living in swift-moving, well-aerated mountain streams. The pond dweller will often have a fin on its back and tail, probably also to make breathing easier. For "breathing", as we know, is carried on through the skin as well as the gills.

THE MUD PUPPY KEEPS ITS YOUTHFUL GILLS

Many salamanders start life in the water, and consequently have gills. Later on, as they pass out of the larval stage, they may acquire lungs or breathe through the skin. Others, among them the mud puppies, continue to use their gills all through life.

Some salamanders living in lowland waters—permanent streams, ponds, or lakes—lose their gills; others keep them. The Great Hellbender, *Cryptobranchus alleganiensis*, has gills as a larva, but loses them early in life, even though a gill slit remains on the adult. The fully grown hellbender has lungs but mostly uses its skin for breathing. Similarly the Congo Eel, *Amphiuma*, keeps its gill slits even after outgrowing its gills. But in the Sirens, *Siren* and *Pseudobranchus*, the gills are outside the head and usually are quite conspicuous throughout life.

Among the Tiger Salamanders, *Ambystoma tigrinum*, there are some that may or may not lose their gills. Curiously enough, the Northwestern Tiger Salamander, *Ambystoma tigrinum melanosticum*, is known to breed when still having the outward appearance of the larval stage, with the tail fin and featherlike gills that are ordinarily lost in the adult stage. Similar larvae were first known in the lakes around Mexico City, where they were called by the Aztec name, *axolotl*. The creature attracted so much attention, and became so well known, that the name *axolotl* is universally applied to tiger salamander larvae. Some of the axolotls from Mexican lakes are able to part with their gills and become land dwellers using their lungs for breathing. But the work of the lungs is aided by their moist skin, which absorbs oxygen.

Many of the common salamanders in North America, such as the Red-backed Salamander, *Plethodon cinereus*, and Slimy Salamander, *Plethodon glutinosus*, in the East, and the Arboreal Salamander, *Aneides lugubris*, in the West, have no lungs at all. Such animals "breathe" through their skin or through other body tissues exposed to the air. If these salamanders are examined under a magnifier that enlarges them only twenty or thirty times, the corpuscles (blood cells) moving in the small blood vessels of the skin can easily be seen. The flow of the corpuscles is not steady, for the heart pumps the blood at intervals, causing it to speed up momentarily. Throat movements draw air into the mouth, the lining of which is richly supplied with blood and thus able to absorb oxygen.

Salamanders living in the oxygen-carrying water of swift mountain streams breathe mainly through their skin and require neither gills nor lungs. In fact, lungs might be a handicap because when they were filled with air, the salamanders would find it hard to stay down on their feeding ground in the stream bottom.

Many lungless salamanders never enter the water at all. The red-backed and slimy salamanders mentioned earlier will drown if forced to stay under water.

COURTSHIP AMONG SALAMANDERS

Among salamanders the eggs are commonly (but not always) fertilized as they are being laid. In some cases observers have witnessed courtships of great drama and elaborate ritual. These pave the way for such fertilizations.

The tiger salamanders, for example, conduct a social courtship in which the males arrive first in a group at the breeding site. They move about rapidly in the water, rubbing against one another. This behaviour apparently excites the females, who have followed the males to the meeting place, and prepares them for the actions that result in the fertilization of their eggs.

A SALAMANDER WITH WAYWARD BREATHING HABITS

Some tiger salamanders discard their gills when they become adults. Leaving the water to dwell on land, they breathe through their lungs and absorb oxygen through the moist skin. Others, retaining the gills of the larval stage, spend their adult lives in the water.

The Red Salamanders, *Ensatina eschscholtzii*, court in couples rather than in groups. The male approaches the female stealthily, crouching low as he moves toward her head. Upon reaching her, he massages her throat and snout by rubbing her with his head and neck. This is followed by the "tail walk", in which the male leads the female about, his back arched and his tail between her legs. Finally the male deposits a conical structure of jelly, capped by a packet of sperm. The female, whose throat has been pressed over the hip region of the male, moves forward with him once more. As her vent comes into place over the packet of sperm, she squats on it, drawing it into her body. This procedure was observed and reported by Dr. Robert C. Stebbins.

HOW THE EGGS ARE FERTILIZED

The female salamander retains the sperm in small packets in the roof of her vent. The eggs are fertilized as they pass these pockets when they are deposited. In one salamander the sperm, like tiny tadpoles, move inward and fertilize the eggs in the body cavity of the parent. This would be necessary in the case of a live-bearing salamander such as the European Black Salamander, *Salamandra atra*, which retains the eggs in its body until the young are fully formed. The young are produced in similar fashion by a relative, the European Spotted Salamander, *Salamandra maculosa*, but only if it cannot reach water. Usually its eggs are laid in streams.

The Black Salamander, which bears fully formed offspring, is usually found at relatively high altitudes, on steep slopes where no pools are available.

THE EGG-LAYING SALAMANDERS

The red-backed and slimy salamanders—like the Worm Salamanders, *Batrachoseps*, of the Pacific Coast from Baja California to Oregon— lay their eggs on moist ground under rocks or rotten logs. The young pass through a gilled stage inside the egg, and when they emerge they are fully formed. The red-backed salamander is often found coiled around its small clutch of eggs. The arboreal salamander deposits its eggs in the cavities of oak trees, sometimes several feet above the ground.

Salamanders living in the water ordinarily lay their eggs there. The Two-lined Salamander, *Eurycea bislineata*, lays about thirty eggs. She attaches them singly to the underside of any suitable rock in the mountain brooks that are her home. Several other salamanders that live in mountain springs or brooks follow a similar procedure. The hellbender female, with the largest eggs of any North American salamander, deposits her eggs in two long strings. The male stands by and fertilizes the eggs after they are laid, as many fishes do. The relatively huge, pale yellow yolk of each egg is about a quarter-inch in diameter, surrounded by a transparent envelope nearly three times as large.

SALAMANDERS VARY IN SIZE

Salamanders vary greatly in size. The largest known is about thirty times as long as the smallest. Japan and China boast the largest tailed amphibian in existence, the Giant Salamander, *Megalobatrachus japonicus*. This creature at times reaches a length of over five feet, thereby dwarfing its American relative, the hellbender, which rarely reaches a size of more than two feet. At the other extreme lies the

THE SMALLEST SALAMANDER

The maximum length of a pygmy salamander, tail and all, is two inches. It is a native of the American South-east. At the other end of the scale we find the giant salamander. A creature of the Orient, it is about thirty times as long as the pygmy salamander.

Pygmy Salamander, *Desmognathus wrighti*, of the spruce-forest mountain tops in the south-eastern United States; this small creature's body is barely more than an inch in length. Even with its tail included, the largest adult is hardly two inches long. The two-toed congo eel may reach forty inches, the greatest length attained by any American salamander.

THE SOUNDLESS SALAMANDER

In contrast to the tail-less amphibians, salamanders, with but one known exception, have no vocal cords, and most of them are silent. True, a few squeak or produce faint noises when picked up, but this probably comes from the accidental expulsion of air from the throat in the animals having lungs. In the lungless salamanders it is difficult to explain the noise at all, unless the air is forced from the mouth.

FOOD AND FOES

Insects, millipedes, or similar small creatures form the salamander's diet. Mud puppies and newts occasionally eat fish eggs, but such thievery is unusual. On the whole the salamander leads a harmless existence, as far as man is concerned: not especially beneficial, but certainly not destructive.

House cats and other common animals prey on salamanders, as do crows. Sometimes during their night-time prowls salamanders are seized by small owls. Other amphibians, frogs as well as salamanders, feed on them. Such fishes as bass and pike eat the larvae or the adults; catfish devour their eggs.

Throughout their lives salamanders are subject to hazards of one kind or another. And yet a few may live to a ripe old age. Tiger salamanders in the permanent larval stage have lived as long as twenty-five years. The Great Crested Newt (or Warty Newt), *Triturus cristatus*, of Europe has been kept for twenty-nine years, equalling the hellbender's record. The giant salamander of Asia exceeds all others, however, having passed the half-century mark.

THE HELLBENDERS AND GIANT SALAMANDERS

This family, which includes the largest living amphibian, is essentially a relic from millions of years ago and now contains only three species. It is doubtful whether any marked change in the habits of these animals has occurred for millions of years. All three are largely water dwellers, fishlike in much of their behaviour as well as in their reproduction.

The three members of the family (Cryptobranchidae) hold the record for age and size. They are the Common (or Great) Hellbender, *Cryptobranchus alleganiensis*, the Giant Salamander, *Megalobatrachus japonicus*, and the Ozark Hellbender, *Cryptobranchus bishopi*.

The fossil skeleton of a thirty-million-year-old ancestor of one of these, five feet long, was once mistakenly described as that of a man. This ancestor lived in Europe, where no giant salamanders are now found.

ENDURING FAME

Man's destruction of the forests has caused streams to be filled with silt, making them unsuitable for hellbenders. Man has also polluted streams with sewage or other wastes, and has built dams. Thus man has done much to destroy the breeding grounds of the hellbender and its gigantic relative. These salamanders are anything but handsome, but they are interesting none the less. Yet within the next century they may reach the end of their long career on earth. In any event, their fame as record holders for size and age is not likely to be forgotten.

The Hellbender, *Cryptobranchus alleganiensis*. Imagine the astonishment of the angler pulling his line from the river and finding on his hook . . . a large greyish, or reddish, blotched creature, wrinkled as a dried prune, body flattened from top to bottom, tail flattened from side to side! A fish? No, for he finds four short thick limbs, with four stubby toes on the front two, and five on the hind. Then he will throw it back. As he tries to remove the ugly thing, his finger is painfully bitten by sharp teeth. Finally back in the water, the hellbender speeds agilely for the depths of the river.

Had the angler stopped to examine his "fish" more closely, he would have found a keel from the tail extending on to the body over the hips and a fleshy keel on the back side of each leg. He would have seen a wrinkled fold along the sides of the body reaching from the neck to the base of the tail, and small, lidless eyes close behind the snout and out of all proportion to the hellbender's great length, which is sometimes twenty-seven inches.

We do not know just how the common name "hellbender" originated. Probably it was invented by some early fisherman who made the creature's acquaintance on the Susquehanna River or one of its tributaries. Obviously not a fish, but quite unlike other salamanders, it must have puzzled that early fisherman. "Possibly," the fisherman may have concluded, as he watched the ugly animal swim off into

the depths, "it's a creature from hell, where it's bent on returning."
Whatever its origin, the name has become widespread and, in fact,
almost the only one applied to it along the tributaries of the Ohio
and other rivers draining into the Mississippi as far west as Iowa. So
hellbender it is—one of the more interesting tailed amphibians in
North America.

THE SHY HELLBENDER

Though the hellbender is an amphibian, it does not spend much time on land. Instead, it
favours large streams, where it spends the daytime in seclusion on the river bottom. At
night it ventures forth in quest of food carried by the stream.

The hellbender rarely ventures on land from the rather large streams
that it occupies. Few people encounter it apart from the startled fishermen whose bait attracts the creature. During the day this salamander
usually remains hidden beneath rocks or other objects on the river
bottom, depending largely on the current to bring food within reach.
At night it ventures from its seclusion and feeds in the open water on
the stream bottom.

Mr. Clifford H. Pope and I found hellbenders in the river near
the town of Radford, Virginia. We had learned of the place through
Dr. Paul Burch, who accompanied us to a small dam on the river.
Dr. Burch had found that during the spring, and less often during the
summer months, hellbenders climb out of the water and go upward
over the rocks beneath the framework of the dam. Unable to ascend
farther, they sometimes remain in pools. By peering into these with the
aid of a flashlight we finally found our quarry.

——How the Hellbender Breeds. Whether hellbenders migrate
or move up and down stream at various seasons no one knows for

certain. But some time during the latter part of August, or a bit later, the male removes the sand or silt from beneath the downstream side of a rock. In this bowl-shaped nest the females, for sometimes there are several, deposit their eggs. These are laid in two long strings, resembling strings of beads. The male, guarding the nest, is on hand at the time. From his vent he emits a cloudy, stringy substance containing the male germ cells, which fertilize the quarter-inch eggs after they are laid.

Sometimes over four hundred eggs are laid by a single female. The male may remain with her throughout the incubation period. Over two months later the larvae, now more than an inch long, are ready to escape from the egg capsule. Equipped with gills at first, they swim forth, propelling themselves with their fin-edged tail. Outlines of two toes can be seen on the front limbs, but the hind limbs are mere paddle-shaped lobes directed backwards.

——How the Hellbender Grows. The gills are not lost until nearly a year and a half later, when the larva is four or five inches long. The lungs have developed meanwhile, but they are ordinarily used only during the rare intervals when the creature is on land. The young hellbender breathes through its skin when under water. Oxygen is taken into the blood through the walls of the capillaries, tiny blood vessels that almost reach the surface along the wrinkled folds of the skin. These folds are constantly waved to carry oxygen-bearing water over the skin.

The animal continues to grow, feeding on almost any sort of food that comes its way. It devours insects and their larvae, sometimes even the eggs of its own kind. It is not fully grown for several years. The male becomes broader and heavier than the female of the same length.

Hellbenders are known to be long-lived creatures. One kept in the Amsterdam Zoological Garden was obtained in 1902 and did not die until 1931, after twenty-nine years in captivity.

The Giant Salamander, *Megalobatrachus japonicus*, the largest known surviving amphibian, is much like the hellbender in its habits. Its eggs are somewhat larger, and it lays fewer at a time. It has a prolonged infancy. Its gills remain until nearly three years after hatching and it is not able to breed until nearly a year or more later.

The giant salamander lives in mountain streams of China and Japan and is a popular food among the natives. In Japan it is found only in the higher portions of the island of Hondo. Enterprising Japanese now raise these giants commercially. Years ago Dr. Hugh M. Smith reported that people in the vicinity of Funatsu, especially women, used the meat for medicinal purposes. The meat of the giant salamander is probably wholesome and palatable, but it is of dubious value as a medicine.

Of course, large specimens are a tempting source of food, as they weigh nearly a hundred pounds.

It is probable that this giant has already been exterminated by man in parts of its range. Animals as long as five feet are becoming rare, for they grow slowly.

The fact that there are giant salamanders in Asia (also as fossils in Europe) while their only living relatives, the hellbenders, maintain an existence in the eastern part of the United States, suggests that such creatures formerly lived in many other parts of the world. It is generally believed that at times in the past there was a land bridge that connected Alaska with Siberia. The ancestors of the hellbender may well have reached North America by way of such a bridge and probably lived in much of Canada at one time. Meanwhile, changing climatic conditions and the uses man has made of the animal's native streams seem to have reduced their range to its present limits.

——THE LONG-LIVED GIANT SALAMANDER. Efforts to rear giant salamanders in captivity have not been wholly successful, although six were raised from a pair that bred in Amsterdam. These giants are seldom exhibited in the United States, but many kept in European zoological gardens have lived for years. One remained alive for about eighteen years in the New York Zoological Garden where it died in 1927. Lord Rothschild kept two giant salamanders at Tring Park in England. But because they fought if kept in the same tank, he placed them in separate tanks, where one lived forty years and the other forty-four years.

Major Stanley Flower, to whom we owe much of our knowledge about the duration of life in animals, is reasonably sure that some giant salamanders have survived as long as fifty-five years. This is the greatest age known for any amphibian. It is remarkable, as Major Flower comments, that this salamander, which normally lives in cold, running mountain streams, should thrive in small tanks.

THE NEWTS AND THEIR RELATIVES

The newt, intended captive of many a small boy dangling a worm tied to a string, is a desirable and easily obtainable small pet. You do not have to look for newts in remote woodlands. I have found them in many lakes, ponds, pools, and ditches within a few short miles of New York City. They are safe to handle and fun to observe.

The most interesting fact about the newt is that it lives a double— or rather, a triple—life. It is born in the water, where it lives a few months before losing its gills. It then lives on land for two or three years. Finally in adulthood it returns to the water to breed and live out the remainder of its life, which may be a long one. One great crested newt is reported to have been kept alive in captivity for twenty-nine years.

In its middle land-dwelling life, the newt is called an "eft". Both names are derived from the old English "ewte" for "evete". "A newt" was originally a wrong division of the words "an ewte", in speaking.

TAILED AMPHIBIANS

The tailed amphibians included in the family Salamandridae (newts and their relatives) are at their most varied in Europe, where their history dates back nearly forty million years. The more primitive species are mostly rough-skinned, largely water-dwelling newts which some scientists place in a separate family, Pleurodelidae. The more specialized kinds, such as the misnamed "Fire-salamander" (properly the European Spotted Salamander, *Salamandra salamandra*) spend more of their time on land. The most primitive members of the family are species of the Asiatic genus *Tylotriton*, found in the eastern Himalayas, Yunnan, and Okinawa Island, which gained fame in the Second World War.

——WHERE NEWTS ARE FOUND. Newts are the only salamanders found in Great Britain. In the English language the term "newt" has come to be applied to several closely related salamanders—those ordinarily associated under the name *Triturus*. Members of this group or genus are widespread in the northern half of the world.

Eight kinds or species are found in Europe, seven in the United States. Many more occur in Asia, while the three salamanders known from Africa are all close relatives, including the Spanish Newt

Pleurodeles waltl. The newts on the Pacific Coast of the United States are more akin to those in Asia. The newts in the Atlantic drainage, including the Mississippi Valley, are smaller and more like the newts of Europe.

The Great Crested Newt, *Triturus cristatus.* Late in February or early in March the great crested newt, largest of the three newts of England, crawls forth from the bottom of ditches and ponds, from the warm crevices and underside of logs. It has hibernated there, safe from the winter frosts, since October, perhaps briefly poking its head out during a few warm spells in the winter. In April, if it is of breeding age, it will return to the water for courtship and mating.

The female is some six inches long, slightly larger than her mate. The upper parts of both male and female are mottled purplish black to dark brown, sometimes with black spots. The belly varies from bright orange to yellow, with irregular black spots. When fully grown the male has a high, notched crest or keel on his back, which is separated from a similar crest in his tail. Viewed from the side, this crest has the appearance of a saw with irregular, badly sharpened teeth. This fleshy keel on the back is absent in the female; her tail is provided with fins, or flattened extensions of the skin, smaller than those of the male.

——How the Crested Newt Breeds. In April as a rule, males and females assemble in ponds or quiet streams. The male becomes excited in his movements and lashes his tail, stirring up the water near the female by his agitated behaviour. Finally he deposits a somewhat cone-shaped structure of jelly in front of the female. This contains a packet of sperm, which the female immediately picks up with the lips of her vent. The spermatozoa, or male germ cells, are kept in finger-like pockets in the roof of the female's vent. From there they find their way inside her body where they fertilize the eggs.

The eggs, each enclosed in a flattened ball of jelly, are laid singly. The female usually wraps a leaf about each egg as it is laid, using any sort of water plant to provide this additional protection. A partly transparent, fishlike larva appears about twenty days later; the time required for development depends to some extent upon the temperature of the water. The large-headed larva, with delicate, feather-like gills, eats the tiny animals sharing its pool. Its front legs begin to appear, followed by the hind ones. Finally, by late August, development is complete. The gills are absorbed, and the transparent skin is replaced by an opaque one more closely resembling that of the parents. The salamander is now ready to leave the water.

The great crested newt spends two or three years on land before returning to the water. It breeds almost immediately upon its return, although it may continue to grow until the end of its fifth year.

The great crested newt is more inclined to remain in the water than either the Smooth Newt, *Triturus vulgaris*, or the Palmated Newt, *Triturus helveticus*. All three may sometimes be found in the same pond. Here they prey upon tadpoles, worms, insect larvae—virtually any small object that moves, attracts their attention. Small boys catch them by tying a worm to a piece of string and dangling it in the water. A small piece of meat, as long as it is agitated, serves equally well as bait.

——How the Crested Newt Defends Itself. The crested newt does not hesitate to prey upon its small relative, the smooth newt, or even upon the young of its own kind. But it is itself protected from the appetite of many larger animals by its skin, which is covered with tiny warts or tubercles (that is why it is sometimes called the warty newt). These are actually tiny glands producing a poisonous substance so disagreeable that it repels even those snakes and other animals for whom most salamanders furnish a favourite food.

The American Spotted Newt, *Triturus viridescens*. The common or spotted newt of the eastern United States is easy prey for the newt hunter. Throughout the spring and summer I have found many of them in the ponds of the Palisades within a few miles of New York City, and farther inland in clear mountain lakes or ponds where the adults often congregate. In ponds filled with leaves or other vegetation they are not so easily seen; but once, by raking the leaves from the water's edge in early spring, I found as many as thirty of them in half an hour. The spotted newt is active throughout the day and so is easier to find than many other salamanders that come out only during the hours of darkness.

The spotted newt is slightly more than half as large as the great crested newt. But its manner of living, its life history, and its feeding habits are much like that of its British relative.

——Courtship Among the Spotted Newts. The male of the spotted newt is larger than the female on the average. (We have seen

[10-5, 5A]

The New World warblers number some 110 species, 56 of which occur in the United States the balance being distributed throughout the rest of the Western Hemisphere. For the most part, they are comparable with the Old World warblers in size and song. Many varieties, like the prothonotary feeding his bulky baby (*above*) and the Buchman's warbler (*left*), one of the rarest of North American song birds, are more brightly coloured, however, than the Old World warblers.

[10-5B & C]

The species of American ground warblers are well represented by the ovenbird (*below*) and the Louisiana water "thrush" (*right*). Not to be confused with the tropical bird of the same name, the warbler ovenbird builds an unplastered oven-shaped nest of grass and leaf stems on the ground. Partial to rocky glens and deep ravines, the water thrush builds its nest in a small depression in the bank of a stream. Both birds show the more ordinary warbler coloration and, like all ground warblers, walk rather than hop. See page 1156

Another unmistakable North American bird, the scarlet tanager has a much more limited range than the red-winged blackbird and is found usually in the north-eastern quarter of the United States. Four of the almost 200 species of tanagers breed in the United States but return to the tropical regions of the Americas for the winter. All the males of this widespread family are brilliantly coloured, but the "prize-winner" is a permanent resident of the American tropics, the paradise tanager, which combines velvety black with striking shades of apple green, scarlet, yellow, opal blue and purple.   *See page 1158*

[10-6]   [10-6A]

The 425 related species of finches, buntings, grosbeaks and sparrows make up the largest of all bird families. Dwelling in all parts of the world and endlessly varied in habits, colour and song, they present many problems to the naturalists. The North American goldfinch with its rather melancholy song and roller-coaster type of flight is often called "wild canary" but the domesticated songsters were derived from an Old World species.   *See page 1162*

[10-6B]

The purple finch, which is actually more an old-rose colour, was once rather common in the eastern part of the United States. These birds have moved westward, and north into Canada, with the spread of the introduced English or house sparrow—which is neither a sparrow nor particularly a native of England.

that among the crested newts the female is the larger.) During the mating season the tail fins of both male and female become enlarged, but much more so in the male. He also acquires patches of thickened black skin on the inner side of his thighs and the tips of his toes, which he uses to seize the female following courtship.

There is one peculiar aspect to the courtship and breeding behaviour of spotted newts. In the autumn and occasionally at warm intervals during the winter, dozens of them will gather in the ponds to perform mating antics. This is a false breeding, however, for the female will not deposit her eggs until the spring.

The genuine mating activities follow the spring migration to the water. The newt, having spent from two to three years on land as a red eft, is now ready to breed. There are profound changes in his skin and in other parts of his body that prepare him for breeding and for his return to life in the water. (In some places, on Long Island in New York, for example, the land-dwelling stage may be omitted.)

Courtship begins with the male moving stealthily toward the female. She may dart away, but the male repeats his approach. Glands in his cheeks expel a colourless substance into the water. This increases the female's interest, and she pauses. Thereupon the male becomes agitated and goes through a series of contortions. He rubs the side of his head against the snout of the female. Suddenly he seizes the female, grasping her from above at the shoulder region with his hind limbs. While he holds the female securely, he may sit with her on the bottom of the pool for several hours.

Finally they are ready to complete the mating. The male deposits as many as three disclike gelatinous masses. An oval packet of male germ cells is attached at the upper end of a thin cord that rises from the disc.

This packet is picked up by the female and the eggs are fertilized in much the same manner as in the crested newt. The eggs are also deposited in a similar fashion, one at a time, and fastened to leaves or plants in the water. Only a few eggs are deposited each day until a total of two hundred or more have been laid.

——HOW THE SPOTTED NEWT DEVELOPS. The eggs hatch within a month, more or less, depending upon how cool the water remains. Usually in May the larvae break the transparent membranes surrounding the eggs and free themselves. They are then about five-eighths of an inch long, light yellowish green in colour, with a faint grey line on either side of the spine. After about two months the larvae are nearly an inch and a half long and ready to lose their gills, as well as the keel on the back and the tail fins.

At first, respiration or "breathing" is carried on through the gills and the skin. As its lungs develop, the larva begins to use them, coming to the surface for air. When the gills are finally absorbed, the newt leaves the water. At this stage its skin is light yellowish, reddish brown or even olive green. But gradually it changes to bright red, with a row of black-bordered vermilion spots on each side of the back. It is now a red eft. Its skin is thickened and rough, no longer suitable for water-breathing. It now breathes solely through its lungs.

On land the eft wanders about in cool, shady places, usually in wooded areas. Sunlight is not entirely shunned, for the eft can stand more heat than can other salamanders. But during dry weather it seeks the seclusion of moist crevices. Following rains, or on occasions when the weather is foggy, it stalks its prey at any hour of the day or night, feeding on mites, spiders, insects, worms, and small snails.

——EFTS VARY IN SIZE. The eft looks for moist places underground as the cold winter months approach. At elevations of four thousand feet in the Adirondacks in New York its active growing season may be short, but in the lowlands from Louisiana to Florida along the Gulf Coast, it is probably active the year round. Yet newts from the South are smaller than their northern relatives. Because of these variations and slight differences in colour, they are considered to be a race or subspecies of the spotted newt of the North.

Some people grow more rapidly or become taller than others. And this is also true of newts. Again, their size varies from one locale to another. Dr. Sherman C. Bishop measured a number of red efts he captured one August in the woods near Cossayuna Lake in Washington County, New York. He found they could be separated into three groups. Those that he believed to be in their first year on land were about two inches long. Some were a trifle smaller, others larger. Some that he thought were in their second year on land averaged a half-inch longer. Those in the remaining group, about three inches long, were supposedly in their third year on land and ready to return to the lake where they had begun life.

——HOW THE EFT PREPARES TO RETURN TO THE WATER. The newt resumes its water-dwelling existence four years, more or less, after it leaves the egg. Its life cycle is complete: it is now ready to mate—

to start the next generation on its way. Before the eft reaches the water, or often after it arrives, its skin again begins to change colour. The bright red skin slowly turns to greenish olive. The roughened skin once more becomes smooth and fit for "breathing" under water, even though the eft continues to use its lungs. Its tail, rounded while on land, now grows fins.

———What the Spotted Newt Feeds On. The return to the water is marked by changes in the spotted newt's food habits. As a water-dwelling salamander it must now find its prey in pools or streams, feeding on small water beetles, caddis fly larvae, leeches, worms, and fairy shrimp, depending largely upon what is most abundant. Dr. W. J. Hamilton of Cornell University has found that newts are efficient destroyers of mosquito larvae. During late March he discovered newts eating the eggs of the Spotted Salamander, *Ambystoma maculatum*. Newts also devour their own discarded skin, a thin transparent cover that is shed at intervals.

Because of their destruction of mosquitoes the spotted newts may be considered beneficial to man. Upon rare occasions they devour small fish, and possibly their eggs; but the damage is not serious. Newts are interesting to study and observe, and few salamanders are so easily kept in captivity.

THE LUNGLESS SALAMANDERS

The majority of the American tailed amphibians belong to the family Plethodontidae, whose name derives from the Greek and means "full of teeth".

All members of this family lack lungs, and they all possess a groove extending from each nostril to the lip. This structure, the nasolabial groove, has no apparent use beyond serving to drain water from the nostril. The family is the only one that has succeeded in invading South America. Except for one species of the genus *Hydromantes* that lives in the Alps and on the island of Sardinia, the family is confined to the New World.

Those that live in the United States include the arboreal salamander, which, as its name indicates, lives mostly in trees; and the green salamander, a cliff dweller. The arboreal salamander is found on the Pacific Coast, while the green salamander dwells in the Appalachian regions.

The Arboreal Salamander, *Aneides lugubris*. I saw my first arboreal salamander in a gold mine in California. I was about fourteen years old at the time and with some other boys I had walked up into Millard Canyon below Mount Lowe in the San Gabriel Mountains behind Pasadena. Here there were several abandoned mine shafts that had been dug into the granite walls of the canyon. We had candles and we found a can with which we improvised a lantern. Then we entered what we judged to be the deepest tunnel because it had the largest pile of rocks near the entrance.

Water from small cracks in the jagged roof trickled to the floor of the tunnel from where two rivulets of clear water flowed toward the outside.

As we moved into the depths of the shaft I was startled to see something wriggle in the water. Directing my makeshift lantern toward the source of the movement, I saw the shiny, dark body of a salamander. Farther back in the mine we found two more.

Carrying these with us, we hastened to the exit. Outside in the bright sunshine we examined our captives. They were stout-bodied creatures about six inches long. Their smooth brown skin had a sprinkling of yellow dots along each side of the body. Grooves in the same regions gave the body a ribbed or corrugated appearance. The head broadened noticeably behind the eyes, which were located well forward on the head. One of the salamanders squirmed in my hand, and I felt faint scratches as the teeth from its overhanging upper jaw scraped over my fingers.

I was astonished to learn, some months later, that the animal was called the arboreal salamander. Later on I found others, usually under boards or the bark of wet, decaying logs. On the hill above the Los Angeles River in Elysian Park I discovered two under flat rocks that I had overturned in search of centipedes. Why was an amphibian that lived in such places called the arboreal salamander?—a name implying that it lived in trees. Of the many I had found, not one was in a tree.

Some years later when I was in college I found the answer in a book. More than a hundred of these salamanders had been discovered by workmen cleaning out the rotted wood from the holes of the live oaks on the campus of the University of California at Berkeley. Along with salamanders they had found twelve clutches of eggs. Fortunately, Dr. Loye Miller was on hand while this work was being done. He had tried many times before to find these salamanders during the dry summer months.

Encouraged by this fortunate disclosure of the animal's breeding habits, Dr. Miller soon learned a great deal more. The arboreal salamander had been described a half century earlier, during the year that gold discoveries brought the "Forty-niners" flocking into California. But little was known about it before Dr. Miller's investigations.

A SALAMANDER THAT LIVES IN TREES

The arboreal salamander, a six-inch creature that has no lungs but gets its oxygen through its skin and the lining of its mouth, spends most of its life in trees. A fine climber, this salamander is able to curl its tail about tree limbs. It deposits its eggs in tree cavities, sometimes as high as twenty feet above the ground.

——HOW THE ARBOREAL SALAMANDER DEVELOPS. The drama of the arboreal salamander's early development can be observed through the transparent envelope that covers the egg. Limb buds, later to become legs, appear first in front and then at the back. A few days later the gills, which will disappear even before the young animal has hatched, begin to grow. These are flattened and branched, the blood coursing through them in tiny vessels as the heart beats. They continue to grow and expand over the embryo, which is curled around the yolk, its food supply. Several days later the transient gills begin to disappear and are finally lost as the tiny animal assumes the adult shape, eventually becoming a fully formed salamander within the moist egg membranes.

Mr. Miller found that though the arboreal salamander sometimes lays its eggs on the ground, it more often deposits them in cavities of oaks—occasionally as high as twenty feet above the ground. The eggs are fairly large, sometimes three-eighths of an inch in diameter, and each is attached to the roof of the cavity by a slender, gelatinous thread. From twelve to nineteen are laid, and usually an adult is found coiled around them. Eggs are deposited during the months of July and August, when the ground in California is baked and dry. Perhaps the animal locates its "nest" in oak trees because the crevices have a certain amount of moisture. It has been suggested that the coiling of the mother's moist body around the eggs keeps them from becoming too dry to develop.

Evidently the mother remains in close contact with the suspended capsules. Perhaps she guards them from raids—even from others of her kind. Adult individuals brought into the laboratory sometimes devour their own eggs.

When the inch-long salamander hatches after two months or so, its body contains a small store of food left over from the yolk. On coming out of the egg, the young cluster together, which helps to prevent them from becoming too dry. Soon the autumn rains of the Pacific Coast bring the moisture that allows them to leave their "nest". They descend to the ground where they may feed throughout much of the winter before next summer's drought again drives them to shelter— perhaps in the trees, or to such wet places as the old mine tunnel where I first saw them.

However, there can be little doubt that arboreal salamanders spend a good deal of their life in trees. Their toes are somewhat flattened and broader at the tips, suggesting that they may be used like the adhesive pads on such climbers as the Tree Frogs, *Hyla*.

Also, the arboreal salamander can curl its tail around a limb, the way an opossum does, to hold on as a precaution when climbing. The tail of other land-dwelling salamanders is easily fractured, which sometimes distracts the attention of an enemy from the salamander itself. But the tail of the arboreal salamander is not easily broken. It is usually curled in a spiral to one side while the creature is at rest.

——How the Arboreal Salamander Gets Its Food. The arboreal salamander forages at night, possibly on trees as well as the ground. It eats insects, including ants and various kinds of beetles. Dr. Miller has found pieces of wood and fungus in the waste matter of animals recently captured. He believes that fungus growing inside the cavities of the oaks inhabited is occasionally devoured during the summer months, when the outside air is too dry for the salamander to leave its home.

The arboreal salamander, like all members of the Plethodontidae family, has no lungs. It breathes through its skin and may besides draw some air into its mouth by throat movements. Dr. Miller has heard two individuals utter a mouselike squeak, possibly caused by the expulsion of air from the throat.

The animal's teeth, easily felt by rubbing a finger over its snout, are dagger-shaped and extraordinarily large for its size. Adults sometimes bite at a stick or a finger thrust in front of them. This show of fight may be of importance to females guarding their eggs.

——Relatives of the Arboreal Salamander. The arboreal salamander has few close relatives. There are two on the Pacific Coast of the United States, one in the Sacramento Mountains of New Mexico, and a fourth in the Appalachians between West Virginia and Georgia. The last of these is known as the Green Salamander, *Aneides aeneus*. It is one of the most beautifully coloured of all salamanders.

The habits and life histories of the green and arboreal salamanders are very much alike, though their ranges are two thousand miles apart. Each has acquired the coloration and form that fit it for survival under the conditions where it now lives. Yet their common mode of existence, with few changes, has evidently been handed down from some ancient common ancestor.

Professor E. D. Cope found one of these salamanders in Nikajack Cave in Tennessee and named it *aeneus*, meaning "bronzed", because of the blotches of greenish yellow that adorn its back and sides. Its colouring blends with that of the lichens that grow on cliffs and trees and may protect it from the eyes of its enemies.

For it seems to be essentially a cliff dweller, whether the cliff be of limestone, sandstone, quartzite, or granite. A green salamander has turned up in a woodpile in North Carolina, and others have been found beneath the loose bark of dead trees. The eggs were first found in a cavity of a fallen limb of the water-oak by Mr. Clifford H. Pope. More recently the green salamander has been found breeding in the horizontal crevices of granite cliffs in North Carolina.

The female green salamander selects damp but not wet places where the temperature is about 65° Fahrenheit, to lay her eggs. She lays as many as twenty-three, each suspended by strands of mucus from the top of the crevice. The mother is always on hand and often lies coiled around the clutch. The young hatch in something over two months, and on two occasions the parent has been found with her recently hatched young.

The most impressive aspect of the life of salamanders and related creatures is their adaptability—their size varies from two inches to five feet; some have gills, some have lungs, some breathe through the skin; some live in the water, some on land, some underground, some in trees. This adaptability is what we would expect from a group that has maintained itself for 340 million years.

The Frogs and the Toads —Amphibians without Tails

FROGS are so common and so widely distributed that most of us make their acquaintance at an early age. If they were rare creatures, or confined to some distant outpost, we might well look upon them as marvels of nature. In many respects that is just what they are.

The salamander waddles along slowly, rather crudely, twisting its body from side to side as its feet move outward and forward. The more efficient toad hops along much more rapidly. The frog, in one swift leap, dives from the shore on the approach of an enemy. Such methods of travelling, or of eluding capture, may be the chief reasons for the survival of the tail-less amphibians. The name of their order Salientia, means "leaping animals". This flourishing group can scarcely be called defeated. Frogs have not achieved the emancipated state attained by birds or mammals—or even reptiles. Still, there is no reason to believe that the group is waning.

HOW TOADS DIFFER FROM FROGS

The name "toad" is commonly used to refer to any of several closely related animals belonging to the genus *Bufo*. Toads breed in water but spend much of their time on land, sometimes miles from permanent pools. Their skin is usually rough. It is moist, but not slippery with mucus.

But there are other tail-less amphibians that seldom stray far from water. They forage along creek or river banks, in pools, marshes, or sloughs. Their skin is commonly smooth, well lubricated with mucus, and feels wet to the touch. Such animals are known as "frogs" or as "true frogs" and belong to the genus *Rana*. This Latin name has been retained unchanged in Spanish, so that in Spain and Latin America a frog is still called a *rana*. The toad is called a *sapo*, however, the original Latin name *Bufo* having been corrupted in the course of time.

In contrast to the group names *Bufo* and *Rana* for several closely related kinds of animals, the popular names "toad" and "frog" are used indiscriminately. Members of the genus *Hyla*, which often live in trees, are interchangeably called "tree frogs" or "tree toads". Some pointed-nosed burrowers that live in the south-eastern portion of the United States are called either "narrow-mouthed frogs" or "narrow-mouthed toads". The Surinam Toad, *Pipa pipa*, of South America, is always called a "toad" despite the fact that it is strictly a water-dwelling animal and hence more like a true frog.

Common or vernacular names, therefore, are largely a matter of convention. They are often merely the designations coined by travellers or writers who have felt the need for some simple way of talking about a particular animal. But all tail-less amphibians, when spoken of collectively—as the whole assemblage—are "frogs". The Midwife Toad, *Alytes obstetricans*, of Europe, and the British Toad, *Bufo calamita*, popularly called the "natterjack", for example, might be included in a list of the "frogs of Europe".

TOADS

Toads are among the most interesting and most familiar amphibians. But familiarity does not always result in understanding, and folklore notions about toads tell us more about people than about toads. Hence the familiar myths that toads produce warts, and that it sometimes "rains" toads.

As we shall see later on, scientific study has distinguished between truth and fancy in describing the life of the toad.

The toads form one of the dominant families (Bufonidae) among the tail-less amphibians. According to some authorities, the toad family has as many as seven subfamilies. The family Bufonidae includes many common species as well as some with the most bizarre specializations. The Mexican Burrowing Toad, *Rhinophrynus dorsalis*, for example, is a sharp-nosed, pink-and-brown species that feeds largely on termites. Then there is the so-called "robber frog" of the genus *Leptodactylus* (widespread in the Americas). Unlike most toads, the "robber frog" has teeth, and many authors prefer to separate this and some related genera as a distant family, the Leptodactylidae.

Toads in the scientific sense (the species of *Bufo*) live in most parts of the world and are about as well known as any amphibians. Formerly they were absent from Australia and the islands of New Guinea, Madagascar and a few others; but one kind of toad or another has appeared in many of these areas—brought there by man in his efforts to control insect pests. There are three kinds in Europe, two of which are found in England, and well over a dozen in the United States. Toads live in mountains, valleys, or plains, from Alaska to the tropics. They live in forests or in deserts, almost any place where there is a warm summer and sufficient fresh water to enable them to breed.

HOW TOADS BREED

The toad does not need more than a temporary, often very shallow pool, but its eggs must be laid in water. In temperate regions the breeding season usually coincides with the spring rains. The first April downpour brings out the American Toad, *Bufo terrestris americanus*, in great numbers. Each has spent the winter in a secluded spot underground, often some distance from water. After dark the males make their way to a suitable pool, frequently crossing ditches or other water to reach the breeding site.

A TOAD THAT KNOWS ITS WAY HOME

The American toad is famous for its homing abilities. It has been known to return to its breeding site after being carried a mile away. Scientists who have studied this toad believe it is guided by the droning calls of its fellows in the "home" breeding pond.

We do not know exactly why the male toad finds one place attractive and another unattractive. But nearly always he calls from a place that is going to be suitable for the female to deposit her eggs. As a rule, the pond or stream selected will not dry up before the young can hop away. Occasionally a toad makes a mistake, but it is evident from field observation that the site chosen usually comes close to the ideal for breeding purposes. Sometimes newly created man-made ponds are used, while other times a previously satisfactory pond may be abandoned. Thus it is obvious that the toad's choice depends upon existing circumstances.

HOW THE TOAD ATTRACTS A MATE

There is no real courtship among the tail-less amphibians. However, the voice plays an important part in their mating. The first male toad to reach an acceptable pool begins to call. He inflates a balloon-like extension of his throat by expelling air from his lungs. The mouth and nostrils are kept tightly closed, for the toad does not use his lungs for breathing while he is calling. Air is driven back and forth over the vocal cords, between the lungs and the mouth. The whole animal vibrates as the sound produced is magnified in the distended throat, or vocal pouch, which serves as a resonator.

The melodious drone of the male American toad carries some distance and attracts the female. He seizes the first female to appear, climbs on her back, and grasps her firmly with his fingers. During the breeding season his thumb and inner finger are provided with dark horny growths—the nuptial pads. These enable him to hold on when other suitors appear. They may attempt to dispossess him, but ordinarily the first toad to seize the female is the one that remains to fertilize her eggs.

HOW THE EGG DEVELOPS

The American toad, like most others, lays as many as eight thousand eggs in two long strings of jelly. The female expels the eggs as she moves about, and the male on her back fertilizes them as they reach the water. The eggs hatch within three days if the water is warm, but it may take nearly two weeks for them to hatch if it is cold. The tadpoles, like those of most other toads, are black.

Gills appear on the outside early in the development of the tadpole. But they disappear when a fold from the head grows back to cover them. Water is drawn into the mouth, passes over the gills inside the head, and out through an opening, called the spiracle, at one side.

A black horny beak surrounded by rows of horny combs at the front serves as a mouth. During the next two months the tadpole feeds frequently—mainly on vegetation which it rasps from plants growing in the water. Though the tadpole is essentially a vegetarian, it also relishes dead animals, including other tadpoles.

As to growth, hind limbs appear first, followed by front limbs. Its tail becomes progressively shorter at the same time that its lungs are developing. It never gets teeth, but bony jaws form, and a more ordinary mouth replaces the horny beak and combs. The fully formed toad is now ready to move to land, even though its tail may still not be completely absorbed.

The toadlet remains near the water for a long time. It hides by day and comes out to feed at night if the weather is dry and warm. It devours small insects or their larvae, centipedes, spiders—in fact almost any small animal that moves. The toad misses any prey which, though still alive, does not move.

Taking advantage of rains and travelling at night in order to conserve the water that would be lost through evaporation, the small toads scatter out from the breeding site. Some may be killed accidentally or devoured by enemies. Eventually each survivor finds a suitable shelter, often in a garden or a cultivated field. Feeding voraciously, mostly on insects, the toad is probably mature and ready to breed by the beginning of its third year. Thereafter its growth slowly tapers to a halt. Males rarely exceed three and a quarter inches in length; females may be an inch longer.

The Carolina Toad, *Bufo terrestris terrestris.* The American toad ranges throughout the eastern United States and south-eastern Canada. In the extreme South-east it gives way to the Carolina Toad, *Bufo terrestris terrestris.* This one is similar to its northern relative, but has a pair of knoblike projections above and behind its eyes. I have studied the habits of the Carolina toad at the Archbold Biological Station in Florida, where the species was abundant. On the basis of the samples secured there, I estimated that nearly eight hundred toads of this species live in the immediate vicinity of the station.

——THE CAROLINA TOAD'S HOMING ABILITY. The northern representative breeds from early in April through July. In central Florida the season is much longer, starting in March. I found the Carolina toad breeding throughout the summer, as late as mid-September. Following summer showers I heard these toads calling in great numbers from pools just outside my quarters. I kept a record of the number I could find each night, and if there had been no rain during the day, few toads were **abroad**. The heavier the rainfall, the more toads I found.

One night after five inches of rain had fallen, I collected nearly two hundred toads in about an hour. I marked these and many others so that I could recognize them when I saw them again. Then I carried them away in different directions from the pool near the laboratory where I had captured most of them. I freed forty-three toads a mile away, and later found eight of them quite near the laboratory. I had carried them across a cleared area free of toads, and so it is doubtful that any of them had ever been in the area. How did they find their way home?

I could not answer this question for certain, but by studying all the facts I could gather, I concluded that these toads had probably been guided back to the home site by the chorus of voices that still echoed from the breeding pond. Many others in addition to the ones I found must have returned home, for it would not have been possible for me to find all of them.

I also discovered while working at the laboratory that toads apparently come out at intervals to feed for a while and then disappear again, even though the weather may be suitable for them to remain abroad. Presumably they retire underground.

One night I found a toad sitting on the pavement near a building at the Archbold Laboratory. I picked it up and examined it, noticing that it had two toes grown together on the right hind foot. Because I was nearing the end of my stay, I merely tossed the toad a few feet back from the road.

The following night, as I made my rounds, I noticed a toad sitting in the same place as the one I had seen and examined the night before. I captured it and found it to be the same one with the toe deformity. During the next two weeks I encountered this deformed toad in almost the same spot night after night. Only once did I fail to see it.

Here was a toad that came at the same hour every night to the same spot on the pavement. It was not there earlier in the day, or I would have seen it. By day it was gone, but night after night it reappeared. How long it continued to come to this feeding station I can only guess because I had to leave after two weeks' observation.

The Oak Toad, *Bufo quercicus*. In this same region of Florida there is another, much smaller member of the group—the oak toad.

It is rarely longer than an inch and a quarter. The shrill call of this tiny toad is well-nigh deafening. When a chorus was close by, I seemed actually to feel excessive pressure on my eardrums.

The breeding habits of this smaller toad are not unlike those of its larger relative. However, the oak toad deposits its eggs in small rods of jelly, from two to six in each rod.

The Desert Toad, *Bufo punctatus.* In the arid South-west of the United States there is a toad of medium size that deposits its eggs singly rather than in the characteristic string. This is the desert toad, whose call is a melodious trill resembling the noise produced by the common cricket. The desert toad ordinarily inhabits rocky areas and its body is flattened. This is useful when the toad is seeking shelter in crevices.

It does not always secrete itself among rocks, however. At the bottom of the Grand Canyon in Arizona I once overturned a wooden keg that had been placed under a trickle of water. Over a dozen toads were packed solidly beneath its wet bottom. Outside, the ground was dry, and I had seen no toads. On other occasions I saw them appear in considerable numbers immediately after a summer thundershower.

MYTHS ABOUT TOADS

The appearance of toads under such conditions has given rise to a widespread belief that it "rains toads". Indeed it is not impossible to gain the impression that they have come from "out of the nowhere, into the here". But certain it is that they have not come from the sky! Doubtless the presence of moisture has merely given them the signal to come out of the crevices or burrows where they have hidden in order to avoid the drying effects of the desert air.

The belief that "toads cause warts" is another common superstition. This ridiculous notion apparently results from the assumption that the "warts" on the toad's skin are contagious. As a child I often caught and handled the toads that appeared in irrigation ditches on our ranch in Colorado. The workmen and visiting neighbours would admonish me: "You'd better not play with those. You'll get warts!" Ignoring their not-so-sage advice, I continued to handle toads, and my repeated experiments never produced the dire effects my elders predicted. I am sure that my parents never believed the superstition, and perhaps they relieved my worries.

It was not until later that I learned that the "warts" on toads are actually small glands that produce a poison. If there are no cuts or abrasions on your hands, you can hold most toads without danger. However, if the poison enters a cut, or if it gets into the eye, it can cause an intense irritation.

POISON GLANDS FOR DEFENCE

Such glands in the toad's skin are scattered over the upper surface, one over each shoulder usually being much larger than the others. The poison produced by these "warts" discourages many attackers. Dogs sometimes make the mistake of believing the toad to be a harmless plaything. However, when seized the toad proves to be a bitter mouthful. The dog froths at the mouth and the way he behaves makes it clear that the toad's poison is effective.

Far more severe effects result from the poisons of some of the larger species of toads. The Colorado River Toad, *Bufo alvarius*, living in the desert regions near the mouth of the Colorado River, occasionally reaches a body length of seven inches. Its greenish grey skin is smooth, with few glands or "warts" on it. This toad has the usual enlarged gland over each shoulder, in addition to some on the arms and the legs.

Dogs that attacked these giants of the genus *Bufo* have been known to die from the effects of the poison. We need further investigation, since it is not certain whether the deadly substance is swallowed or whether it enters the dog's blood stream through the thin skin lining the mouth. It has even been suggested that vapour from the poison is inhaled or drawn into the lungs of the unsuspecting dog.

TOADS AS PEST EXTERMINATORS

A toad with such a deadly way of protecting itself might be considered dangerous to have around. This is not the case, however, for if the toad is not mistreated, it can be picked up and handled without causing its captor any discomfort. While I was working in Arizona one summer, my family and I stayed in a house that was inhabited by scorpions. There were not a great many, but we had found one or two every night. The ordinary scorpion has a sting little worse than a bee's, but these were the kind that sometimes produce severe symptoms.

In an effort to reduce the number of scorpions, I kept two Colorado

One of the few completely red birds and the only one with a crest, the cardinal belongs to a group of finches best known in South America. The females have the crest and the red bill but are much duller in colour. Although it does not migrate and the northern winters are very hard on it, the cardinal has gradually extended its range as far north as the Great Lakes.

See page 1163

[10-7]

The white crowned sparrow (*left*) ranges throughout the southern half of the United States (with the exception of a small portion of the south-east) through Mexico and into Central America. The tree sparrow (*below*) breeds in the Canadian Arctic and spends most of its time in the northern half of the United States. Small but sometimes aggressive, sparrows as a whole are very adaptable, and many of them are good singers.

[10-7A & B]

The painted bunting is a species more familiar in the southern United States but members of this group have wide distribution over the North American continent, many of them wintering in Central and South America. Many brightly coloured birds seem to disappear before the times generally stated for their migratory flights because they moult their distinctive plumage in the late summer and grow duller and more drab feathers. The buntings are no exception.

[10-8]

While the bills of the sparrow family are for the most part stout, conical affairs well adapted for cracking seeds, the grosbeaks as their name implies carry this feature to an extreme. Evening grosbeaks (left) do not restrict their activity to the evening hours as might be expected. Like the cardinals these finches are gradually extending their range north and eastward. The male rose-breasted grosbeak (below) is one of the "gems" of the family. About the size of a robin, it has a somewhat similar but more melodious song.

See pages 1163, 1164

[10-8A & B]

[10-9]

[10-9A]

The weaverbirds (to which family the house sparrows belong) are highly sociable, exclusively Old World birds, most of the 260 species making their homes in the tropics. While the group is generally best known for its expertly constructed hanging nests, some species do not make nests at all but lay their eggs in those made by other more industrious weavers.   See page 1164

Averaging about 12 inches in length, the blue jay delights in noisily tormenting owls and foxes, and its boldness carries over to the defence of its nest —it will launch a courageous counter-attack against a marauder many times its size. The omnivorous blue jays seldom migrate and their bright blue and white plumage is especially handsome against a landscape of snow in their northern range.
                                                        See page 1178

[10-9B]

[10-9C]

Scattered in pairs or small groups during the spring and summer, American crows gather to roost in great flocks during the winter. By day they radiate a distance of 20 or 30 miles from the roost in search of food—and they eat almost anything. Many naturalists consider the resourceful crows and the closely related ravens the most highly evolved and the cleverest of all birds. Largest of the family Corvidae which includes the jays, rooks and magpies, these two birds are at home throughout most of the world, adapting to and surviving in areas where their smaller cousins were not successful in establishing themselves.   See page 1176

Magpies are Oriental birds but the attractive, shining bluish-black and white common magpie has made its way as far as the arid western plains of North America via Siberia and Alaska. As their mixed diet includes fruits, melons and other crop plants as well as young poultry and game birds, they are not generally regarded with much favour.
                                                        See page 1179

The American cedar waxwing is one of three species whose scientific family name means "little silky ones". The other two species are the Japanese and Bohemian waxwings, and the plumage of all three is exceptionally soft and silky. These birds are considered songless as they utter only reedy, lisping notes. American waxwings make up for the fruit they eat by consuming enormous quantities of harmful cankerworms. *See page 1170*

[10-10]

[10-10A & B]

Many birds are known for their skill in constructing nests but the bowerbirds of Australia and New Guinea are the master builders. The intricately designed bowers which cover several feet square are often ornamented with shells and bits of coloured glass, and are basically places where the males display to attract mates—the nest, which is quite ordinary, is usually placed some distance away. The building habit is so ingrained in these birds that they work at bower construction most of the year, not just at mating time. While they lack the amazing plumage of their close relatives, the birds of paradise, many male bowerbirds, such as the regent (*right*), are brilliantly coloured. Even the eyes of the satin bowerbird (*below*) are blue. *See page 1186*

River toads on the front porch, where the scorpions had been most often encountered. I provided water for the toads in a pan, where they sat during the day, coming out at night to hop about the concrete floor of their screened enclosure. While I was away on a trip the pan became dry and I returned too late to replenish the water. With no moisture to replace that lost through the skin, the toads were nearly dead when I arrived. One toad rallied when I put it in water, but the other was so dried out that it could not be revived. When I examined it to see what it had been eating, I found five scorpions and two crickets in its stomach. Evidently, therefore, the poor creature had been doing the extermination job I had set for it.

The Neotropical Toad, *Bufo marinus*. The Colorado River toad is exceeded in size by the neotropical toad, one of the most abundant and widely distributed toads in the American tropics. This Goliath

A GIANT AMONG TOADS

The neotropical toad is the colossus among the tailless amphibians in the Americas. Large females are sometimes as much as nine inches long and six inches across with the limbs folded. The giant toad has been introduced throughout the tropics to control insects infesting sugar cane plantations.

among tailless amphibians in the Western Hemisphere reaches its greatest size in northern South America. A female with a body length of nine inches was taken in British Guiana by Mr. Robert Snedigar. The specimen, the largest one known, is in the collection of the American Museum of Natural History.

This great toad has a range extending southward from southern Texas through the lowlands of Mexico to Brazil. Its parotoid glands, those over the shoulder, are enormous. If the toad is irritated, a milky secretion oozes from the pores of the gland. After Dr. Albert P. Blair liberated some of these toads in a pond in southern Texas, a turtle appeared and seized one of them from below. The toad, with its lungs inflated, could not easily be pulled under. As the turtle continued its attack, Blair saw the poison appear on the surface of the gland, and the turtle abruptly dropped its intended prey and departed.

The success of the neotropical toad, as indicated by its abundance, can be attributed in part to the protection the poison glands afford. The majority of the frogs, *Rana*, are not so well equipped. The Pickerel Frog, *Rana palustris*, is an exception, with a skin so well lubricated with poison that other amphibians placed in the same container with it are likely to succumb. Most frogs avoid their enemies by means of a sudden leap into the water.

THE TRUE FROGS

The biography and habits of the common frogs (*Rana*) are fundamentally pretty much the same as those of the toad. The male frog of each species has a distinctive call, no two kinds being identical. In each case it serves to entice the female of its kind to the breeding pool. Here the eggs are fertilized in somewhat the same manner as those of the toad. However, frogs do not lay their eggs in long strings. Generally they deposit their eggs in a single clump and anchor them to plants growing in the water.

Permanent pools or lakes are usually preferred. The size of the egg cluster and the place selected for laying the eggs vary from species to species. Some kinds can endure low temperatures better than others. From the north-eastern United States westward throughout most of Canada, the Wood Frog, *Rana sylvatica*, is among the first amphibians to appear during the spring. This is one of the smaller frogs, little more than three inches in length. I have observed wood frogs breeding in March when ice was still in the ponds, and the water was only a few degrees above freezing. Such frogs lay relatively small clumps of eggs, a thousand or so, usually a few inches below the surface.

The family Runidae includes our common bullfrog. It is primarily an Old World group, with the greatest number of species in Africa. In the New World, as well as in Australia, there is but a single genus, *Rana*. Several species live in Canada, the United States, and Mexico, but only one has reached South America. There are numerous genera in Africa, especially in the rain-forests. The famed "Hairy Frog", *Astylosternus robustus*, is a ranid, the male of which has hairlike extensions from the skin on the thighs and flanks. Apparently these do the work of gills, and compensate for the greatly reduced lungs of this frog. The largest tailless amphibian now living is a gigantic ranid in Africa.

The American Bullfrog, *Rana catesbeiana.* In contrast to smaller kinds, the American bullfrog does not ordinarily deposit its eggs until much later in the year, in June or July in the northern part of the United States. By this late date the surface of the water may have reached 70° Fahrenheit. In the South breeding occurs much earlier. The huge egg-mass contains as many as twenty thousand eggs— according to Dr. A. H. Wright, one of the few who has ever undertaken the task of counting them. The eggs spread out in a film on the surface of the water. Exceptionally large masses cover five square feet.

——THE SIZE OF BULLFROGS. Bullfrogs were originally native to eastern North America, from Canada southward to the Coatzacoalcos River at the Isthmus of Tehuantepec in Mexico. Because the legs of this large frog are in considerable demand as food, the bullfrog has been widely introduced throughout the western part of the United States as well as into other parts of the world. In the South the female, the larger of the two sexes, attains a body length of eight inches. In the North seven inches is closer to the maximum, and such sizes are the exception rather than the rule.

The bullfrog is the largest tailless amphibian in the United States. Elsewhere it is exceeded in size, notably by the Giant Frog, *Rana (Conrua) goliath*, of the Cameroons and the Gabon region of west Africa. The giant frog may measure as much as a foot or more in length, and weigh as much as a large domestic cat. It lives in deep forest streams, where natives are seldom able to capture it except during the dry season when the water is low.

Bullfrogs require permanent pools partly because the tadpole may take as long as three years to transform. Legs rarely develop during the first summer, but under ideal conditions they appear early during the second year. The astonishingly large tadpole may be half a foot long before the tail begins to be absorbed. However, when ready to depart from the water, minus its tail, and no longer a tadpole, the animal measures slightly more than two inches in length.

——WHAT THE BULLFROG FEEDS ON. The bullfrog spends two to three years on land before it reaches adult size. The younger frogs depend largely upon insects for food, but almost any animals small enough to be eaten fall prey to the adult. In many ponds crayfishes form a large proportion of the frog's diet. Presumably the frog captures these bottom-dwelling crustaceans while under the water. On land the bullfrog overpowers and eats salamanders, toads, frogs, small turtles, snakes, mice, and even birds.

——THE BULLFROG'S ENEMIES. On the other hand, a number of other animals prey upon the bullfrog. As a tadpole it is attacked by such insects as the giant water bug. This water-dwelling insect uses a tubular, needle-like snout to extract the body fluids of the tadpole. Fish undoubtedly eat the eggs and larvae, as well as the younger

THE AMERICAN BULLFROG AND ITS ENEMIES

The American Bullfrog is the largest tailless amphibian in the United States. The female, larger than her mate, reaches about eight inches in length. She lays about twenty thousand eggs at a time—a fortunate provision against the frog's many enemies. A particularly dangerous foe to the tadpole is the giant water bug, equipped with a needle-like snout to extract body fluids from its victim.

frogs. We may assume that the tadpole is not spurned by birds that normally eat fish. Large bullfrogs may be cannibalistic; they not infrequently attack and devour smaller frogs of their own kind.

Man has become one of the bullfrog's principal enemies. Because these valuable amphibians were in danger of extermination, they are now protected in some of the American states. During a single year, however, nearly three-quarters of a million pounds of frogs' legs were marketed in Louisiana alone. It is doubtful whether all of these were from the bullfrog. Other large frogs, especially the Southern Bullfrog, *Rana grylio*, may have been included in the catch.

OTHER FROGS

Frogs live in all continents, although they are far more abundant in the northern half of the world. Nearly twenty kinds are found in the United States alone, and there are half a dozen additional species in Mexico. Only one of these ranges into South America, probably because this continent was cut off from North America at the time that frogs were first becoming numerous.

The Leopard Frog, *Rana pipiens*, a spotted species, as implied by its common name, is the most widely distributed of any species in North America. It covers the area from coast to coast and ranges southward from Canada to Panama. I have found it in the Pine Barrens of New Jersey, in irrigation ditches in Colorado, and in the streams of California and Arizona. With Dr. A. F. Carr, Jr., I collected specimens near the edge of the cloud forest on Cerro Uyuca in Honduras at an elevation of five thousand feet, and we found it at much lower levels near the margins of Lake Yojoa in the same country. In Costa Rica the leopard frog has been seen in the meadows on the slopes of the great Irazú volcano.

Where there is enough water, leopard frogs manage to live even in deserts. We found a fair-sized population around an isolated spring coming out of a limestone mountain in the middle of the desert in the Mexican state of Coahuila. This group, cut off from others by the intervening deserts, included some specimens with spots, and others that lacked them completely. After capturing thirty of them, however, we found a nearly complete gradation from only a few spots on some creatures to many spots on others.

This variation, or the marked differences that exist between individual animals, is both a source of confusion to the amateur and a source of interest and study to the professional biologist. Changes in climatic conditions over long periods of time may give one individual an advantage over another. Thus, a prolonged period of drought will cause the death of many individual frogs that are less able to resist dry conditions. Others in the same population may, through the accident of inheriting suitable traits, be better able to withstand long periods of dry weather.

HOW NATURAL SELECTION WORKS

In the long run, therefore, the animals that survive will be the ones that live long enough to breed. They will pass on their characteristics to some of their offspring, which thus stand a better chance of survival. Members of the population with unfavourable characteristics are "weeded out", so to speak. During the course of many generations changes will result—changes that enable the surviving frogs to live under increasingly dry conditions in their surroundings. This weeding out of the unfit, coupled with the survival of individuals better adapted for life in the region in which they live, is known as *natural selection.*

SPECIALIZATION AMONG FROGS

Similar processes have brought about a great many changes in the frog's pattern of living. Very often these changes have affected the frog's breeding habits or its life cycle. Through the changes resulting from natural selection, some frogs have managed to overcome the handicap that makes it impossible for any but the more specialized kinds to breed on land. Eggs laid in water are at the mercy of all sorts of hazards; ponds may become dry, fish or other amphibians may eat the eggs. Some kinds of insects deposit their eggs inside those of amphibians, and the grubs that hatch devour the yolk.

There are advantages to be gained, therefore, by depositing eggs where they are not exposed to such raids. One of the tree frogs of Mexico deposits its eggs in the moisture-catching leaves of an air plant that grows on the trunks or limbs of trees. The tadpole manages to move about in somewhat the same fashion as a worm, feeding on the food available, on the wet surface of the leaves of the air plant. It gradually acquires the legs and lungs of the adult without ever going near a pool. Hence this frog is able to live in regions where there are no ponds or streams.

THE WATER TOADS

The water toads, with only four genera and a handful of species living in Europe, Asia, and the Philippines, make up a family of little importance. The one exception in this family (Discoglossidae) is the midwife toad, so called because the male takes care of the newly laid eggs. True, several distantly related amphibians provide parental care, but few are quite so well known as the midwife toad of Europe.

The Midwife Toad, *Alytes obstetricans.* Instead of resorting to the water to breed, the male calls from an entrance to a hole, or burrow, made by himself or appropriated from a rodent. His call attracts the mute female, and several males may gather about her. One male, competing with others, finally grasps the female around her waist.

This embrace may be continued for nearly half an hour while the male strokes the region surrounding the vent. Finally the female extends her hind limbs, which together with the bent hind legs of the male, form a receptacle for the eggs. She expels them in two strings, with several dozen in a set. Each egg is rather large, as much as three-eighths of an inch in diameter. After these eggs have been delivered, the male shifts his body forward, and clasps the female's head as he fertilizes the eggs.

After a pause, he thrusts one leg and then the other through the mass of eggs. When found carrying the eggs with him, the male looks as though the eggs had been wound around his limbs. Meanwhile, the female, her work completed, goes her way, while the male departs with his precious load and returns to his burrow. From time to time during the following nights he comes out to feed, with the eggs still attached to his limbs. Moisture from the dew is absorbed by the eggs on such occasions. The toad may even enter the water carrying his encapsuled offspring with him.

After twenty days or more the larvae within the eggs are well advanced in their development. They have been nourished by the large yolk and the external gills have already disappeared before the male parent carries his load to some pool or stream. This time when they are dipped in the water the larvae burst the soft, gelatinous coverings and take up life in the water. Thus the eggs as well as the tadpoles in their early stages have been protected from enemies, thanks to the male parent's carrying them with him into his burrow. He has also kept the eggs moist through his efforts.

THE MIDWIFE TOAD—A MODEL FATHER

The male midwife toad becomes attached, literally, to the eggs of his mate. After the female lays her eggs, her mate fertilizes them and then thrusts his legs through the mass of eggs. He carries them around with him, while the female goes unconcernedly on her way. For some three weeks the male takes care of the eggs, keeping them attached to his body all the time. Thus they are kept moist and also protected from enemies until they finally hatch into larvae.

FROGS WITH BUILT-IN NURSERIES

Some tropical frogs have other ways of carrying their eggs. For example, the parent may carry the eggs in a single mass on its back. The South American Frog, *Rhinoderma darwini* (family Rhinodermatidae)—named for Darwin, the naturalist who discovered it while he was on his famed voyage in the *Beagle*—carries the deveioping eggs in its vocal pouch. Presumably the male picks up from five to fifteen eggs after they have been laid and fertilized. But he does not swallow the eggs. Instead, they pass through a small slit on each side of his tongue to reach his vocal pouch. The parent carries the eggs in this internal nursery until the fully formed young hatch and depart by way of his mouth.

Some tropical forest frogs, *Phyllobates* and *Dendrobates* (family Dendrobatidae), carry their tadpoles on their back. Dr. Charles M. Breder observed them doing this in Panama. Forest frogs feed during the daytime, moving about constantly in pursuit of their insect prey. Near his camp at Yavisa, Dr. Breder collected a male transporting tadpoles, which were arranged in alternate directions, packed on his back like sardines in a can. The male carries these larvae to pools or to streams where they are able to find their own food.

The Marsupial Frog, *Gastrotheca* (family Hylidae), of South America, has a somewhat more elaborate method of caring for the developing young. The female of this tree frog hides the eggs completely in a pocket on her back. When the young are fully formed, the eggs hatch while still in the purselike pocket. Shortly thereafter the tiny frogs leave the parental shelter through a slit at the rear of the pouch.

THE TONGUELESS TOADS

Many land-dwelling amphibians use their tongues to snare their prey and draw it into the mouth. But frogs that feed under water find little use for either their tongue or eyelids, and these have been lost by most members of the group (family Pipidae). The family consists of only four genera—three in Africa and one, the amazing Surinam Toad and its relatives, in South America.

Frogs belonging to other families, have arrived at ways of caring for their young, including the "built-in nurseries" just mentioned. But the Surinam toad has evolved a truly unique method of carrying its eggs. The creature has so many other highly specialized traits that it deserves our close attention.

The Surinam Toad, *Pipa pipa.* Few amphibians are as famous as the Surinam toad, which carries its eggs in individual chambers in the skin of its back. In this instance, as in the case of the marsupial frog, it is the female that carries the eggs. When she is about to lay them, the female extends from her vent a long, tubular structure called an ovipositor. This is carried forward on her back by the male, who presses on it as the eggs come out one by one. The eggs stick to the skin where each gradually sinks into a separate pocket that forms to receive it. Each of these chambers is covered by a lid apparently developed from portions of the egg capsules. Some weeks later tiny replicas of the adults appear, having gone through all the larval stages sealed in the cavities of their mother's back.

——THE REMARKABLE QUALITIES OF THE SURINAM TOAD. The Surinam toad is a remarkable creature in many other respects. Its entire body is flattened, especially the triangular head. Its eyes, which are extraordinarily small, are situated on the upper surface behind its truncate snout. ("Truncate" means square or even, as if cut off.) There are odd, fleshy projections at the angle of its tongueless mouth. Each of its fingers has a four-pointed, starlike tip. Its hind toes are very long and connected with webs to form broad paddles that propel the animal when it swims, which it does with amazing speed. The Surinam toad probably never leaves the water of its own accord. On land it is clumsy in its movements and nearly helpless.

The animal is so unbelievably different from other tailless amphibians that when Mr. C. B. Perkins placed one on exhibition in the San Diego Zoological Garden, he had person after person come to his office to tell him that "the Surinam toad out there is upside down"!

The creature sits on the bottom with its long fingers spread out on either side of its mouth. Food detectors are apparently located in its starlike finger tips. When they touch some appetizing prey, the toad lurches forward with its mouth open and engulfs it.

Mr. Robert Snedigar told me how he had watched the Surinam toad feed in the quiet pools where he found it near the Essequibo River in British Guiana. A small muscular flap that hangs down over its lower jaw from the snout is kept constantly in motion. The resemblance of this flap to a squirming worm apparently is sufficiently deceptive to entice within reach the armoured catfishes that live in the same pools. Snedigar saw the fish approach the "bait", coming in contact with the tips of the fingers as it did so. This was the signal for the toad to lunge, engulfing the head of the fish in its wide mouth.

Curious to see what else the toads might have eaten, Snedigar and I examined the stomach contents of the preserved specimens he had sent to the museum. The examination confirmed his description, for all we found were the partly digested remains of the armoured cat-fishes. It probably takes other food on occasion, to judge by observations of Surinam toads kept in an aquarium. None the less the curious structure of the fingers, coupled with the angling device, suggests an extreme specialization for a diet made up largely of fish.

Few amphibians are quite so restricted to water as the Surinam toad. However, another member of the same family, the African Clawed Toad, *Xenopus laevis*, seldom ventures on to land. This African relative is not nearly so bizarre in appearance, but it is unique among amphibians in having horny, rather lizard-like claws at the end of its toes.

FROG HABITS AND HABITATS

The tailless amphibians tend to specialize. The Tree Frogs, *Hyla*, with their broadened toes, are well adapted for their climbing existence. They do not confine their movements to shrubs or trees, however. Some of them, such as the Canyon Tree Frog, *Hyla arenicolor*, live in boulder-strewn canyons in the arid South-west of the United States. They blend so closely with the granite or sandstone rocks to which they cling during the day that it is difficult to make them out.

In general tree frogs are most abundant in such humid areas as Florida and the Gulf Coast. More kinds of frogs, *Rana*, are found in regions with heavy rainfall than elsewhere. In contrast, the toads, *Bufo*, being less dependent upon water, are more diversified in the dry South-west. There are six kinds of toads in Arizona, for example, but only three tree frogs. Florida, on the other hand, has only two kinds of toads, but supports seven tree frogs.

Few places in the world can boast the frog choruses to be heard in Florida. One evening at the Archbold Biological Station near Lake Placid nearly a dozen kinds of frogs were calling within a few hours' time. In addition to the oak toad and the Carolina toad, there were three frogs, *Rana*, the Cricket Frog, *Acris gryllus*, the Narrow-mouthed Toad, *Microhyla carolinensis*, and four kinds of Tree Frogs, *Hyla*.

Each of these was breeding; each had its own distinctive call. That of the narrow-mouthed toad resembled the bleat of a young goat. The cricket frog, despite its name, *gryllus*, from the Greek word for "cricket", actually produced a sound more closely resembling the note of the katydid. The call of the tiniest of them all, the Midget Tree Frog, *Hyla ocularis*, was a shrill "pe-teet", scarcely audible above the din produced by the two toads.

The Gopher Frog, *Rana capito*, was calling early in the evening but it was so wary that my companion, Dr. Raymond B. Cowles, and I could not approach it. We found some leopard frogs, and I was inclined to believe that this was the species we had heard. Finally, in the beam of our light we saw a gopher frog before it ducked below the surface. It swam several feet and then hid in the debris on the bottom of the pool. It was not until after midnight that the voice of the leopard frog was added to the chorus.

In Florida's summer rainy season it is not unusual to hear so many frogs calling simultaneously. In New England frog choruses are heard principally during the spring. There is a rather definite order of appearance. The Spring Peeper, *Hyla crucifer*, is invariably first, followed by the leopard frog. The wood frog is next, but there may be a few days' delay before the voices of the American toad, the pickerel frog, and the northern tree frog are heard, in that order.

The best time for capturing and studying the tailless amphibians is during the breeding season. The only equipment you need is a flashlight and a sack in which to carry the specimens. You should wear some old shoes that you do not mind getting wet—for you may have to wade into the water. But a few hours' work on a wet spring evening may provide enough frogs to stock your vivarium for the rest of the year. (A vivarium, by the way, is a moderate-sized enclosure, usually with glass sides, for keeping such animals indoors.)

Reptiles, Survivors of Past Glories

REPTILES have the distinction of being the first back-boned animals that succeeded in laying eggs on land.

As far as we now know, the amphibians had been on solid earth for some fifty million years before one stock slowly changed its structure and its ways and became a reptile. This creature was the first that did not have to deposit its eggs in the water. The young no longer had to pass through the swimming tadpole stage we find in most frogs today. The reptile had overcome the handicap that tied the amphibian to the pools of its fish ancestor. And instead of laying eggs with a tiny yolk the reptile produced relatively large eggs, with sufficient food stored in them to permit the young to emerge fully formed, and ready to go about their business on land. Reptiles belong to the class Reptilia ("creeping animals").

It seems almost ironic that, having taken so many years to acquire the ability to breathe air and remain on land, some reptiles should later return to the water. However, some of them did return, and fittingly enough found that strong bonds now held them to the land—where they had to lay their eggs if the young were not to drown. One long extinct group of fish-eating reptiles, the shark-shaped ichthyosaurs, gave birth to fully formed young. This is also true of some of the modern sea snakes, which consequently do not have to go ashore.

But the gigantic marine turtles that glide so efficiently through the ocean depths are forced to make pilgrimages to the shore. Here they dig a cavity in the sandy beach and deposit the eggs, deep enough to hide them but not deep enough to prevent oxygen in the loose soil from readily reaching the porous covering of the egg.

1239

REPTILES ARE COLD-BLOODED

Like other land dwellers, reptiles get their oxygen from the air. First they take in oxygen through the walls of a sacklike growth from the rear end of the developing embryo in the egg. Later on, after their lungs have developed, they breathe in oxygen. Moreover, in the course of their becoming land dwellers, the reptiles lost the moist glandular skin of their amphibian ancestor and acquired a scaly covering for their body. This thickened skin protects them from enemies and prevents evaporation of their body fluids. These are the reasons why the reptile was the first backboned animal able to venture far from water, and eventually to invade even the driest of deserts.

The reptiles that remained reptiles, that is, those that gave rise to the dinosaurs and to our modern crocodilians, turtles, snakes, and lizards, never developed the ability to produce their own body heat. Some other branches of the reptilian group did acquire this ability; these continued the separate trends that eventually led to the birds and mammals. But the reptiles continued to depend upon the heat obtained directly or nearly directly from the sun.

The reptile is frequently called "cold-blooded" because it derives virtually all of its heat from sources outside its body. Little if any of the food it consumes is turned into heat. Even so, by sitting in the sunlight, or by pressing its belly against rocks or sand warmed by the sun, a lizard can absorb enough heat to raise its body temperature to relatively high levels. When it is active during the day a lizard is able to keep its body even warmer than that of many mammals and birds. Some lizards prefer to have their body temperature in the neighbourhood of 104° Fahrenheit, higher than that of a human being. When the weather becomes too cold such reptiles are forced to retire underground where enemies or freezing temperatures cannot reach them.

None the less there are some compensations in being cold-blooded. A man merely sitting in a room with the air temperature at 60° or 70° Fahrenheit uses up approximately forty times as much energy, largely to keep his body temperature at 98.4°, as a lizard were it of similar dimensions and not active. Rodents, bears, and some other mammals in cooler climates retire for the winter ("hibernate"). Reptiles in such regions do likewise, but, as their requirements are so limited, reptiles are able to live for much longer periods without nourishment. Many of the smaller lizards, snakes, and turtles have remained alive for as long as a year without food. A large python has been known to survive for over three years without eating.

HOW CLIMATE AFFECTS REPTILES

The fact that reptiles cannot heat their bodies internally does, however, place restrictions on them: they cannot live in the colder portions of the world. Snakes are among the most cold-tolerant of reptiles; yet there are only twenty-two kinds or species in Canada in contrast to the 126 in the United States. None range so far north as Alaska in North America. In the Old World one European viper is encountered, it is true, slightly farther north than the Arctic Circle; but this is in the Scandinavian Peninsula, where a warm ocean current tempers the climate of the adjacent land. No reptiles are found where the subsoil is permanently frozen.

In general, reptiles are larger in tropical regions where they are represented by an abundance of species. It is doubtful whether many more remain to be discovered and added to the total of approximately seven thousand kinds or species now known. In the United States about 275 kinds or species are recognized, while all of Europe, lying somewhat farther north than the United States, contains only 103 species, including the five marine turtles that visit its shores.

SIZE AND SURVIVAL

Many more reptiles existed in the past. For some 160 million years reptiles dominated the world, in one sense. By modern standards some achieved the stature of giants. One ancient group even acquired somewhat batlike wings and took to the air. Another group took on body contours similar to those of the shark, with paddle-like limbs resembling fins, and took to the sea; here they preyed upon the relatives of their now remote ancestors, the fish. Still others sought sloughs and shallow waters where they could feed on the vegetation growing on the bottom or along the bank. On the other hand their cousins, the great flesh-eating tyrannosaurs, or "tyrant lizards", walked upright and remained on land, where they killed and devoured their reptilian relatives for sustenance. In short, the reptiles probably invaded all portions of the globe that were warm enough to allow them to be active. The ancient reptiles may not have required so much warmth as many of the present-day kinds.

But seventy or eighty million years ago reptiles went into a rapid decline. Perhaps it was in some obscure way due to the arrival of the mammals with their more advanced methods of caring for their young, and their ability to remain active in nearly all kinds of weather. Or perhaps there were violent climatic changes that were unfavourable for such bulky creatures as the dinosaurs and their relatives that had remained dependent upon outside sources for their body heat.

EFFECT OF CLIMATE

We may never know why the dinosaurs and their relatives perished, but it is possible that the climate became too warm for them. A creature the size of a rhinoceros or an elephant would have had great difficulty finding shade, let alone seeking cooler shelter underground. On the other hand, reptiles the size of most of our common lizards would have found it easy to cool their bodies by retreating into rock crevices, or by digging holes, as many of them now do in the hottest regions.

Large bodies of water do not gain or lose heat so rapidly as land does. If the extinction, or failure to survive, of the large reptiles came about through extensive climatic changes, those living in rivers, lakes, or oceans may have been less severely affected. And so it is probably significant that the heaviest and largest reptiles in existence are creatures that live in rivers or oceans.

THE BIGGEST REPTILES ALIVE

The crocodilian cousins of the gigantic reptilian rulers of the past managed to survive, and today they are the largest reptiles in existence, at least as far as weight is concerned. Some pythons may exceed the largest crocodilians in length, but probably never weigh more than four hundred pounds. In contrast, some of the largest crocodiles may weigh more than a ton. For obvious reasons few of the really large ones have been weighed. Some sea turtles weigh over three-quarters of a ton. The weight of a Pacific Leatherback, *Dermochelys coriacea*, captured off the coast of Santa Barbara, California, is recorded as 1,575 pounds. Even greater weights may be attained.

At any rate, most of the living reptiles are not large creatures. In general the largest ones live in the warmer oceans, or in tropical regions

[10-11]

Efts are a land dwelling phase of the small salamanders known as newts. For the first few months
after hatching they live in the water, completely
aquatic animals with gills; then they lose their
gills, leave the water, and spend the next two or
three years on land. The common or spotted newt
of the eastern United States is a brick-red colour
with black-bordered vermilion spots during its
land cycle, and consequently is known as the red
eft. Some species of newts skip the eft phase.

See page 1210

[10-11A]

Newts mate only in the water and as the eft approaches this stage various changes occur, including the development of a broad swimming tail;
they live out the balance of their lives in the water,
but the gills are never restored. The red eft becomes an olive green newt with yellowish under-
parts. Newts are found throughout the world and
it is interesting to note that those dwelling on the
Pacific Coast of the United States are more akin
to those in Asia, while the newts in the Atlantic
drainage, including the Mississippi Valley, are
smaller and more like the newts of Europe.

See page 1210

[10-11B]

The statement that salamanders are amphibians
with tails is about the only generalization that can
be made in connection with this widespread family.
The red-backed salamander, a species seldom exceeding three inches in length, is found in leaf
mould and under rotten logs in the north and central portions of North America. It is one of a group
of species that breed and lay their eggs on land;
in such cases the young usually pass through the
gill stage inside the egg and hatch fully formed.
Some salamanders bear live young. *See page 1199*

[10-11C]

There are more than 125 species and subspecies
of salamanders in the United States alone, and
many more in Mexico; different varieties are fairly
numerous in Europe and Asia, but only three are
known in Africa and there are none in Australia.
Ranging in size from the two-and-a-half-inch four-
toed salamander of the north-eastern United States
to the five-foot giant of the mountain streams of
China and Japan, many are gaudily marked with
spots and streaks like this small marbled salamander of the swamps of the south-eastern United
States. Others are more conservatively coloured,
the cave and cavern dwellers being for the most
part colourless and ghostlike in appearance.

See page 1194

Many species of frogs and toads—the amphibians without tails—are found on all continents and most are highly specialized. The several varieties of tree-frogs range in size from three-quarters of an inch to two inches. All are equipped with sticky suction pads on their toes, enabling them to walk up window panes as well as trees and shrubs. These two are stalking the moth which was attracted to the window by the light.

See page 1234

[10-12]

The blue colour of this green frog is a trick of Nature, not of the camera—it lacks the skin pigment necessary to produce the hue from which the species gets its name. Closely related to the more common bull frog, the green frog is smaller but quite similar in habits, both living solitary lives in ponds and swamps. The bull frog is the largest tailless amphibian in the United States, but it is exceeded in size elsewhere, notably by the giant frog of West Africa which may measure a foot in length and weigh as much as a large house cat.

[10-12A]

Three stages in the growth of a leopard frog. A newly hatched tadpole is usually so shapeless that the head is best determined by watching the direction in which the tiny animal swims. Gradually the head and gills take recognizable form, but the gills are soon enclosed in a membrane and function internally until they are replaced by lungs. As the lungs develop the legs appear as "buds"—the hind ones first—and the tail becomes smaller. While very similar, the tadpoles of the many species can be distinguished. See page 1231

[10-13]

[10-13A]

The half-grown frog still sports its tadpole tail. The tails do not drop off—they are gradually absorbed as the amphibian matures. Unlike toads, frogs for the most part complete the major part of their growth before leaving the water and as some species, such as the green frogs and bull frogs, take two or three seasons to mature, more permanent ponds and streams are required as breeding places. The leopard frog develops comparatively rapidly and can manage with very little water.

[10-13B]

Ranging in size from two to four inches, the leopard is the most widely distributed frog species in North America. It is found from coast to coast, from Canada to Panama; it often inhabits moist, grassy meadows (hence its other common name, "meadow frog") and, in spots where there is enough water, even manages to live in the deserts.

Toads are generally distinguished from frogs in several ways although the names are often interchanged in common usage. Toads usually have a rough skin and although it is moist it is not slippery like that of a frog; for the most part they are more heavily built, and not as good at jumping. The tiny oak toad of the south-eastern United States rarely measures more than one and a quarter inches, but its shrill call can be almost deafening.
See page 1224

[10-14]

[10-14A]

American toads, a species common in eastern North America, hibernate in secluded spots often some distance from water, and the first spring downpour brings them out in great numbers. Except for breeding and laying their eggs, toads do not actually enter the water but they are amphibians and must keep moist to live. Their sudden appearance immediately after a heavy rain gives rise to the fable that it is "raining" toads.
See page 1220

[10-14B]

The four well-distributed species of spadefoot toads have large, horny spadelike warts on their fleshy feet. Toads' warts are not contagious—they are glands which, on rough handling, secrete a poisonous fluid for the toads' protection. Since one species or another has been introduced into Australia, New Guinea and Madagascar in attempts to control the insect populations of these lands, toads are now found throughout the world.
See page 1220

where cold winters are unknown. Contrary to popular belief, it is never so hot in the tropics as it is in the desert regions farther from the equator, in what are so ineptly called the "temperate zones". The dozen or so principal groups or Orders that formerly existed have dwindled to four. These are the crocodilians, the turtles, the lizards and snakes (the latter two belong to the same major group or Order), and the *Rhynchocephalia*, of which all members but one, the Tuatara, are known only as fossils.

The Crocodilians—Living Giants

THE ALLIGATORS, caimans, crocodiles, and gavials together comprise the group known as the crocodilians, which includes the largest reptiles in existence. They are found in rivers or along the margins of oceans or in lakes throughout most of the tropics, as well as in the warmer, moist regions of the temperate zone. Although only twenty-five kinds are recognized, several of them are abundant in certain localities. They are an important group of reptiles, apart from the commercial value of their hides which are widely used in the leather industry.

All of them dwell in water, where they prey upon a vast variety of other animals. Those with long slender snouts live in India and the Malay region. They are known as Gavials, *Gavialis*, a corruption of the Hindu name *gharial*. The true crocodiles are more widespread, and occur in all continents except Europe and Antarctica. All of them have a few teeth in the lower jaw that are larger than the others and that fit into notches on each side of the upper jaw. This gives them the grinning appearance that distinguishes them from the alligators, whose enlarged teeth fit into pits in the upper jaw. Crocodilians make up the order Crocodilia.

THE ALLIGATORS AND CAIMANS

The existing crocodilians are divided into only three families, Gavialidae, Crocodilidae, and Alligatoridae. The gavials are sparsely distributed in India, the Malay Peninsula and the East Indies. Crocodiles are found in suitably moist regions throughout the tropics. The alligators, which together with the caimans of Latin America, make up the family Alligatoridae, are largely restricted to the New World. The only exception is the Chinese Alligator, *Alligator sinensis*, which is now nearly extinct.

The American Alligator, *Alligator mississipiensis*. Prior to the coming of man, alligators were extremely abundant in parts of the United States, particularly in Florida. Early explorers described such places as the St. Johns River as being so full of alligators that it might have been possible to walk across, using the 'gators' bodies as stepping-stones, had it not been for the aggressive nature of these large reptiles.

——THE ALLIGATOR'S REPUTATION AS A MAN-EATER. Instances of alligators attacking humans are rare. However, in 1949 according to reports of the Fish and Wildlife Service, an eleven-foot alligator in the Okefenokee (Georgia) National Wildlife Refuge developed the habit of stalking fishermen and visitors along the canal. The Refuge agents roped the crocodilian and turned it over to the Okefenokee Swamp Park, where visitors could study the animal.

Occasionally there are reports of alligators charging small boats, but more often such reports are put forth as pretexts for killing larger individuals, which in some areas are protected by game laws.

——THE THREAT TO THE ALLIGATOR. It has been estimated that over two and a half million alligators were killed in the state of Florida alone between 1800 and 1900. By the turn of the century they were already exterminated in parts of their range. The demand for their hides resulted in their being killed more rapidly than they could reproduce. Moreover, thousands of young were sold as pets, or killed and stuffed to be sold as souvenirs. Fortunately many of the refuges established primarily for the protection of waterfowl contained alligators, and these were also protected. Alligator havens have now been established in Louisiana, Georgia, and South Carolina, with some smaller ones in Florida; and this interesting reptile is no longer in danger of being removed from the face of the earth.

However, despite these efforts at preservation, hunting has greatly
reduced the number of alligators. The remaining animals rarely if ever
survive to reach the great size of eighteen feet observed in some alligators
as late as the beginning of the twentieth century. Alligators of even
half this size are uncommon today, although small ones a yard or so
long can readily be seen, even in roadside pools in Florida. The larger
ones are usually found in lakes or in the deeper rivers.

——How the Alligator Moves and Gets Its Food. Occasionally
alligators are forced to make an overland journey, but as with all
crocodilians their main activities are closely associated with the water.
They swim by means of sinuous movements of their muscular tail, in

THE VANISHING ALLIGATOR

As their tough hide is in demand for a variety of uses, alligators have been slaughtered in
vast numbers in the United States. In Florida alone, it has been estimated, over two million
and a half were killed during the nineteenth century.

somewhat the same general way that a mackerel does, with their feet
playing no important part in the propulsion. On land they are rather
clumsy, slow, and deliberate in locomotion, although they carry their
body high off the ground, with just the tip end of the tail dragging.
When provoked, however, they lunge forward with great rapidity, or
wield their tail as a powerful defence weapon.

During the daytime alligators are usually seen basking; they do

1246 THE CROCODILIANS—LIVING GIANTS

much of their feeding at night. Young alligators eat such crustaceans as crayfish and shrimp, as well as insects. As they grow larger they devour snakes and turtles, fishes, birds, frogs, and muskrats. Cannibalism has been reported. Larger alligators even prey upon raccoons, and reputedly sometimes attack animals as large as a bear.

——THE ALLIGATOR'S FAVOURITE HAUNTS. Alligators make burrows, dens, or "'gator holes" as they are called, in the banks of rivers. These serve as places of retreat during the summer. During the winter they retire to these caves or sometimes sink into the mud, leaving a hole to the surface to permit the limited breathing that is necessary when they are inactive. They cannot tolerate high temperatures. A few minutes' exposure to body temperatures only slightly higher than 100° Fahrenheit is sufficient to cause death. They appear to prefer temperatures between 75° and 85°. In the cooler streams of Florida middle-sized or larger individuals are commonly seen basking at the surface of the water, buoyed by the air in their lungs.

——HOW THE ALLIGATOR BREEDS. The heat of the sun is probably of importance in the incubation of the eggs. Ordinarily only twenty to thirty are laid by mother alligators of the size now attained. Formerly very large females may have laid more than twice that many. The female deposits her eggs in a nest that she makes by gathering vegetable waste and mud. Sometimes the nest may be over a yard high, and more than six feet across. After laying the eggs she covers them with the same sort of waste used in constructing the nest. She leaves a small opening to allow the young to escape when they hatch about eight weeks later.

The mother alligator is one of the few reptiles that remains on guard in the vicinity of the nest. Presumably she prevents such animals as skunks and raccoons from removing the eggs. In bygone days when occasional females may have reached the length of eighteen feet or so, any animal venturing into the vicinity was probably attacked. According to some accounts, the female by means of grunting noises calls the young to her den as soon as they emerge from the egg. However, they apparently remain with the parent for a relatively short time, for small alligators take up residence in smaller, often quite shallow, ponds at least a mile or so from any breeding site. In Florida they sometimes move into fish ponds, or drainage ditches.

——THE ALLIGATOR'S SENSE OF HEARING. The ears of alligators are well developed, but they are hidden under a flap not far behind the eyes that few people notice unless it is called to their attention. If this flap is lifted with the fingernail, as it can be in small captive specimens, a rather large eardrum is disclosed within a cavity. It is evident that alligators hear at least as well as humans. On the Caloosahatchee Canal in Florida the Lockmaster told me that one living near the end of a small pier had learned to respond to a call after it had been fed a few times. To show how well trained the 'gator was, the Lockmaster walked to the end of the pier and shouted, "Toby!" Sure enough, within a few seconds a four-foot alligator emerged from the depths.

——HOW ALLIGATORS DEVELOP AND HOW LONG THEY LIVE. The alligator's growth is relatively rapid at first. An alligator eight inches long when it emerges from the egg will more than double its size during its first year of life. It adds about a foot each year until it reaches a length of approximately ten feet. Thereafter the rate of growth tapers off, with only a few inches being added annually.

No one knows the maximum life span of any crocodilian. However, an alligator has been known to live for at least sixty-eight years, and it is reasonably certain that some exceed a century. None the less there is no actual proof for the claims often made in the show places calling themselves "alligator farms" that alligators attain ages exceeding five hundred years.

Living Fossil—The Tuatara

The Tuatara, *Sphenodon punctatum,* is the sole survivor of an ancient group of reptiles, the order Rhynchocephalia or "beak-heads". The early ancestors of the tuatara were a branch of the main reptile stem that later on led to the dinosaurs. Turtles were already in existence, but few other groups had made their appearance. The lizards came later and gave rise to a number of families as well as to the snakes.

The beak-headed reptiles, however, were not destined to achieve importance. When the dinosaurs were becoming diversified many of them attained great size. The ancestors of the tuatara were neither large nor abundant. As far as we can judge by the limited fossil record, none was ever much larger than a five-foot alligator. However, the beak-heads did become dispersed over much of the earth.

The dinosaurs failed to survive—perhaps, as has been conjectured, because of climatic changes, perhaps for other reasons. The beak-heads might well have followed them into extinction had not the tuatara, in some unknown manner, reached the distant outpost of New Zealand.

THE "LIVING FOSSIL"

Here the tuatara lives among the rocks in a cold climate that few other reptiles could tolerate. At one time it lived on the New Zealand mainland, where the first settlers from England made its acquaintance. The native Maori knew it long before the arrival of the European. It was the Maori who gave it the name *tuatara*. Over a century ago it was given the specific name *punctatum*, meaning "spotted", and later assigned to the genus *Sphenodon* or "wedge-tooths". To scientists it is *Sphenodon punctatum*—a reptile superficially similar to some lizards, which it resembles in being able to regenerate its tail, yet so distinct from them in its fundamental structure that it can be recognized as the only remaining representative of the beak-heads. For this reason it is often referred to as a "living fossil".

Today the tuatara is gone from the mainland, exterminated by man and the animals he brought to New Zealand with him. The only survivors now dwell on some small islets in the Bay of Plenty and in Cook Strait north of Auckland. By day the tuatara lives in a burrow, venturing forth after sunset to feed on snails, crickets and other small animals. Like some other reptiles that are active during the hours of darkness, the tuatara has a voice. Its croak is often heard in the islets where it is now restricted, especially on Stephens Island, which may contain as many as five thousand of these reptiles.

The tuatara deposits its eggs in a depression dug in the earth, sometimes laying as many as fourteen. The young do not hatch until almost a year later, when they break the parchment-like shells and dig their way to the surface. Upon emergence the young tuatara is about four and a half inches long. Its growth is not especially rapid, and no one knows how many years it requires to reach its maximum length of slightly over two feet.

SURVIVOR FROM DINOSAUR TIMES

One of the more amazing survivors from dinosaur times is New Zealand's tuatara. A somewhat lizard-like creature, it is the last of its kind, all of its relatives having disappeared from the face of the earth well over a hundred million years ago. Tuataras are long lived —several are known to have survived over twenty years.

THE TUATARA FLOURISHES IN CAPTIVITY

The tuatara is a long-lived creature. One kept in the Dublin Zoological Garden was still alive after twenty-three years when its age was reported. A fifteen-inch specimen in Upsala, Sweden, was alive after twenty-eight years, although it had grown little if any during that period. It was fed on earthworms and raw meat cut in strips, which it ate willingly. It remained quite lively, occasionally immersing itself in the water in its cage. After years of captivity this individual was quite tame. Mr. William Dawbin, writing in the New Zealand journal of natural history aptly named *Tuatara*, reports that a tuatara was kept in captivity in New Zealand for well over half a century.

The Turtles—Reptiles with Armour

TURTLES are proverbially slow-moving and as they have no weapons of offence—with the exception of the snapping turtles—their preservation for 200 million years strikes us as very puzzling. The secret of their survival lies of course in their tough horny shells which have successfully provided them with shelter and protection. The turtle's shell is both a house and a coat of armour.

THE CONSERVATIVE TURTLE

All the changes that led to the armour took place countless ages ago before there were any crocodilians, lizards or snakes. There were no birds and no mammals. The dinosaurs had not yet appeared. To be sure, amphibians and other reptiles were in existence then—but none bore any close resemblance to anything now living. Over 200 million years ago the turtle alone, of all the surviving groups of backboned animals, had become essentially what it is today. And a turtle it remained, giving rise to the reptiles that comprise the order Testudinata (or Chelonia).

Since that distant time the changes in the structure of the turtle have been relatively minor. The original stock gave rise to more advanced lines—always turtles, for no major offshoots ever occurred. One group, the Side-necked Turtles, continued to protect the head by curling the neck around the front of the body. Another more successful group evolved a better means of protecting the head—by withdrawing it into the shell in a vertical S-shaped arrangement. Still others, the Box Turtles, *Terrapene*, for example, went beyond this. By developing hinges at the front and back of the bottom part of the shell the turtle was able to withdraw its head as well as its tail behind closed "doors".

Some turtles reversed the amphibian-to-reptile trend and returned

1250

to water. A few of these, including some of the larger ones, acquired flipper-like limbs and made the oceans their home. Other turtles took to fresh water, and many more remained on land or alternated between land and water. Turtles succeeded in reaching all continents, but they thrived in relatively few habitats. There are few more than fifty species, including the ocean dwellers, in the United States. In all of Europe there are but seven, although five additional kinds, marine turtles, reach its shores. There have been no land or freshwater turtles in the British Isles in recent times.

THE LOGGERHEAD TURTLE—IT HAD FABULOUS ANCESTORS

The loggerhead's shell is sometimes large enough to serve as a small rowboat. Though loggerheads are not likely to exceed three hundred pounds nowadays, we have evidence that they were much bigger in former times. Their weight may have approached half a ton in the days before they were hunted so extensively along the coast. These monsters had a head almost a foot wide.

The structure of the turtle, with its body encased by the covering of bone and horny plates, has proved adaptable to its environment in some ways, but in comparison with other reptiles it has limitations. Turtles manage to dig burrows, although none actually "swim" through the sand as many lizards or snakes do. Unlike several of the latter reptiles, no turtle climbs trees. And needless to say, none has ever managed to fly—or even to glide, an accomplishment of an ancient group of reptiles and of some lizards and at least one snake in recent times.

All turtles deposit their eggs in holes in the earth, regardless of whether the adult lives on land or in the water. The marine turtles could avoid many hazards if they were able to give birth to fully-formed young. The time and energy required to seek land could profitably be devoted to more useful ends. Many sea snakes, for example, give birth to their young without going ashore. But, as we have seen, all turtles adhere inflexibly to the ancestral egg-laying habit.

So the turtle may be considered a conservative. The encased and armoured body has its advantages—200 million years' worth, we might say, but the limitations are also obvious. Of some seven thousand kinds of living reptiles, scarcely three hundred are turtles. It is doubtful whether they were ever much more numerous. Evidence from the fossil record suggests that there may have been a slight peak of abundance about 100 million years ago. Even if this is borne out by future discoveries it was a doubtful heyday.

TURTLES LIVE LONGER

Turtles are persistent creatures, as stubborn in other respects as they have been in their retention of the ancestral form. Tenacious of life, they live longer than any other backboned animals. There is reasonably good evidence that a tortoise on the island of Mauritius lived for at least 152 years. If it had not been killed accidentally, it might have reached the two-century mark. No bird or mammal can approach this record.

Turtles are more vulnerable while they are still in the egg, or immediately after they hatch. At first the shell is soft, but it hardens within the first few years of life and becomes thicker. It is probable that a good many turtles attain relatively great ages, once they have survived the first few critical years. The Common Box Turtle, *Terrapene carolina*, not infrequently lives for over half a century, and possibly reaches a maximum of 123 years.

TORTOISES, BOX TURTLES, POND TURTLES,
AND THEIR RELATIVES

Turtles, including ancient fossil types, have been divided into eighteen families, half of which are still in existence. Among the more successful of the turtles are those in the family Testudinidae. The turtles commonly seen in the Northern Hemisphere are mostly members of this family, although several representatives have penetrated into both Africa and South America. Most parts of the United States contain one or more kinds of tortoises, box turtles, sliders, or their relatives.

The Box Turtle, *Terrapene carolina*, is a dome-shaped creature, with the plastron, or bottom of the shell, flat and connected by a bridge at the sides to the top or carapace. Usually there is an inconspicuous ridge running the length of the back. The whole bony shell is covered with horny plates about as thick as a thumbnail. Colours vary quite a bit, with yellowish spots, blotches, or stripes on a brown or blackish ground colour. The turtle's head is rather small, the snout ending in a sort of overhanging beak that is notched in some races, and not in others.

Both the front and back of the bottom of the shell are hinged at the bridge. When molested the box turtle withdraws its four limbs as well as its head inside the shell, which can then be closed tightly at both ends. A few other turtles have similar hinges in the plastron, and an African species has the carapace hinged near the middle. None, however, manages to close the shell so tightly as the box turtle does, especially the race in peninsular Florida.

——Where Box Turtles Are Found. Several races or subspecies of box turtles are found in eastern North America, all the way from New England to Yucatán in Mexico. Those in the North usually have four toes on the hind feet, while others in the South ordinarily have but three. The Ornate Box Turtle, *Terrapene ornata*, is a closely related species that dwells in arid regions east of the Rocky Mountains, as well as parts of Texas, New Mexico, Arizona, and northern Mexico.

——The Box Turtle's Size and Colour. Box turtles in the northern region of the United States are rarely more than half a foot long. Ten to twenty thousand years ago they commonly attained greater dimensions, and some extraordinarily large individuals still turn up in one area in northern Florida. Eight inches or a little more is possibly close to the maximum size of any now living. The male, commonly the larger of the sexes, has a concave area in the rear of the plastron, which is flat in the female. The iris, or pigmented area surrounding the pupil, is generally pink or bright red in males, and dull brown, or dark red, sometimes even purplish or grey in females.

——Where the Box Turtle Lives. The common box turtle is usually found in wooded areas, at sea-level as well as at elevations as high as four thousand feet. Primarily this turtle is a land dweller. During the hot summer months, however, it is more likely to be in densely shaded areas along streams. Often it is actually in the water, where it floats keeping its head and the upper third or more of its domed shell above the water. Or it may swim beneath the surface, which it does somewhat more awkwardly than the strictly water-dwelling turtles with their flatter shells.

THE HARDY BOX TURTLE

Turtles have changed little during the past two hundred million years. These sturdy creatures outlive all other backboned animals. The box turtle, a typical member of the clan, has horny plates about as thick as a thumbnail.

——How the Box Turtle Moves About. The box turtle is slow and extremely deliberate on land. Mr. John T. Nichols, who has studied these reptiles on Long Island in New York for many years and probably knows more about them than anyone else, tells me that it took one of them fifteen minutes to travel some forty-six yards. This was its ordinary cruising speed, which he figures is about a mile in slightly more than nine and one-half hours! He believes that a large, active male might possibly go a mile in four hours, but that the maximum speed the best of them could attain would not be much more than a half mile per hour. They could keep up such speeds for short distances only.

——The Box Turtle Sticks Close to Home. Mr. Nichols' observations of these turtles on Long Island show that each leads a more or less solitary life, most of it spent within a rather well-defined area.

The radius of their home territory is usually less than 250 yards but may be as much as half a mile. Adult turtles removed three-quarters of a mile usually return to their home territory, whereas young turtles, under four inches long, are much less inclined to return. In any case, if turtles are taken several miles away they do not attempt to go back. This suggests that they may become familiar with areas somewhat larger than the restricted home territory. But with no landmarks in sight they have no urge to return.

In the course of years, box turtles may shift their home territory slightly; but they show a marked inclination to remain in one area. In order to be able to recognize them later, Mrs. Lucille Stickel marked a number of them living on the flood plane of the Patuxent River in Maryland. At the time of a flood she found several clinging to vegetation, but none had been carried away from the home range. After the flood waters had subsided, virtually every turtle found by Mrs. Stickel was near the place where she had first discovered it. Years ago Oliver P. Medsger told how he had marked a box turtle, and found it thirty-five years later within 150 yards of the original spot.

——THE DAILY LIFE OF THE BOX TURTLE. Within its home range the box turtle wanders at random, but with a strong sense of direction. It burrows in leaf mould at night, always emerging by ploughing forward. It is most active during warm rains, or just after sunrise and before sunset. Box turtles drink with the head submerged while muscles in the throat draw the water into the body. A large individual consumes as much as four ounces at one time.

——THE HIBERNATING BOX TURTLE. Box turtles lose moisture rather rapidly when they are exposed to dry air. A Florida Box Turtle, *Terrapene carolina bauri*, lost nearly one-fifth of its weight during a forty-five-hour period that it was kept in a chamber in dry air at a temperature of 100° Fahrenheit. Like its northern relative, the Florida box turtle goes underground during dry weather, as well as in the winter when temperatures are low. During a hot summer at Yaphank on Long Island in New York, George Englehardt found several common box turtles that were buried from six to ten inches deep in the mud bordering a cranberry bog.

The common box turtle has also been found hibernating buried beneath the surface. In Maryland the site it chose was a gentle slope at the edge of a woods. In warm years the box turtle remains abroad as late as early December, and leaves its winter quarters as early as

1 March. It does not ordinarily begin to breed until the onset of summer.

——THE BOX TURTLE'S BREEDING HABITS. Mating may occur throughout the season when the box turtle is active, but it has been observed more often during the spring and autumn. On such occasions the male follows the female about, biting her shell or exposed skin. He lunges against her, pushing her about in an effort to subdue her. When his advances are no longer avoided, the male finally works his legs into the cavities in front of her hind legs. She grips his hind legs with hers and, with the shell of the male raised to an upright position, the tails are brought together. After the eggs are fertilized a thin, white shell on a parchment-like cover is formed over them and they are ready to be laid. Some turtles produce fertile eggs for as many as three or four years following one mating.

In the District of Columbia, H. E. Ewing observed females digging the nests between 22 June and 14 July. They hollow out a flask-shaped cavity in soft soil, the female invariably beginning the task in the late afternoon or early evening. She anchors her body with her forelimbs and digs with her hind legs, using them alternately. She requires from three to five hours before she has dug to the limit she can reach. Sometimes the turtle encounters a root or a rock, in which case she may discard the site in favour of another.

After completing the excavation the female rests a few minutes before she drops the first egg to the earth loosened at the bottom of the hole. Usually she lays three or four or even as many as eight eggs one by one, covering each with earth scraped from the sides of the hole. She presses the earth carefully on to the eggs, until she has deposited the entire clutch. With the hole nearly filled, she reaches out for the dirt on the surface, packing it down by means of treading movements. When she has finished, the female sometimes voids the contents of her bladder on the spot. She has concealed the site so well that it is virtually invisible.

The eggs, which are roughly one and a quarter inches long and three-quarters of an inch in diameter, are white and elliptical, with thin but hard shells. Incubation requires most of the summer. The hatchling, like most other reptiles, is equipped with an "egg tooth" (not a true tooth, as it is in snakes and lizards) at the tip of the snout, although Ewing found that this was rarely used to slit the covering of the egg. More often the young turtle rips a lengthwise slit, using the claws of its front or hind limbs. Once out of the egg, the hatchling digs its way to the surface, but not necessarily at once.

Eggs ordinarily begin to hatch in September, but some may not do so until late in November. In the northern part of the box turtle's range it is not uncommon for the fully-formed turtle to spend the entire winter inside the nest. Even if it were on the surface, the hatchling would go into hibernation without feeding. Commonly some yolk remains after the turtle is fully formed, and this serves to tide the small creature over until spring.

It is usually extremely difficult to find the juveniles, which are generally about an inch and a quarter long when they come out of the egg. Their small size doubtless makes them less noticeable than the adult. So few of them are found, however, that they must be more secretive than adults. Their growth is relatively rapid, apparently, with almost an inch being added to their length each year. They reach maturity at the end of four or five years, when the female is approximately five and a quarter inches long. On Long Island Mr. Nichols found that most of the common box turtles over five and a half inches in length were males, which evidently tend to be the larger of the two sexes.

——THE BOX TURTLE'S VARIED DIET. Box turtles devour an astonishing variety of food, including both plants and animals. They are particularly fond of mushrooms and toadstools. According to some authors, turtles are careful to avoid poisonous toadstools, but others maintain that the toadstools are eaten. No one has settled the question. Slugs, snails, earthworms, caterpillars, succulent leaves, berries, and even carrion make up portions of the diet. On rare occasions box turtles do some damage in gardens, where they eat tomatoes or strawberries. Young individuals will eat the beetle larvae commonly known as "meal worms", although adults often refuse to eat them. Turtles in captivity have accepted lettuce, melon rinds, bananas, and bread. One captive turtle is known to have lived for an entire year without either food or water, although it must have been kept in moist surroundings at moderately low temperatures.

——THE BOX TURTLE'S ENEMIES. Despite their bony, horn-covered shell, box turtles are vulnerable to the attacks of several dangerous enemies. Skunks not infrequently dig their eggs from the nest, and probably devour a few hatchlings. Sometimes adult turtles become so fat that complete closure of the shell is impossible. Julius Hurter tells how he discovered a large brown rat gnawing at the shell of a live box turtle in Missouri. The poor reptile had been turned on its back and was covered with blood. The rat had bitten through the skin of the hind foot, which could not be drawn into the shell. The turtle probably would have been killed if Mr. Hurter had not interrupted the rat's meal.

In Indiana Glenn Culbertson watched from a distance as a number of hogs came upon some box turtles. Several of the hogs picked up turtles, but only the largest of them succeeded in crushing the shells. Squealing for their share, many of the smaller hogs joined the larger ones in devouring the contents.

On occasion an attacker may not fare so well. W. D. Funkhouser describes a combat that he witnessed between a snake and a box turtle on the Dix River in Kentucky. A water snake seized the head of a box turtle while it was swimming. The turtle quickly closed its shell, catching the head of the snake between the plastron and the carapace. Both animals sank to the bottom of the river, but in a few minutes the lifeless body of the snake appeared on the surface, its head crushed.

The automobile has become an increasing hazard to box turtles. Their broken, flattened bodies are commonly seen on the highways through wooded areas in the eastern United States. The Ornate Box Turtle, *Terrapene ornata*, of the western plains, is killed so frequently by automobiles in some sections that many casualties must be attributed to intentional killing by misguided drivers who go out of their way to run over the slow-moving beasts. In the sand hills of western Nebraska and on into Colorado during the spring, I have driven through areas where dead turtles of this species dotted the highway, sometimes as many as three or four within a mile.

Fires destroy an unknown number of box turtles, particularly in Florida where the burning of hammocks (areas with dense vegetation) is a common practice. A fair number of these turtles apparently manage to burrow into the earth, thereby escaping with their lives but with scorched, mutilated backs. Virtually every Florida Box Turtle *Terrapene carolina bauri*, that I have captured had the bone exposed and the horny shell missing from the middle of the back. Such "fire scars" probably persist throughout the rest of their lives.

[10-15]

[10-15A]

Crocodiles have a few teeth in the lower jaw which are larger than the others and which fit into notches on each side of the upper jaw, giving them the grinning appearance that distinguishes them from alligators. All crocodilians—crocodiles, alligators, caimans and gavials—are water dwellers, the different species of crocodiles proper inhabiting either fresh or salt water in all of the world's tropical regions.
See page 1243

Crocodiles are further distinguished from alligators by their more pointed snouts, those with the very long, slender snouts being known as gavials. Gavials (their name comes from a Hindu word) are sparsely distributed in India, the Malay Peninsula and the East Indies. Crocodiles in general have uglier dispositions and are more agile than alligators, hence are more dangerous. *See page 1243*

[10-15B & C]

Alligators with one exception—the now nearly extinct Chinese species—are restricted to the New World. Once extremely abundant in Florida and surrounding areas, the largest living relative of the dinosaurs was almost exterminated by commercial enterprises but now enjoys government protection. Just the reverse of amphibians, these water-dwelling reptiles must lay their eggs on land as their young would drown. Like other crocodilians, alligators spend much time basking in the sun, or if direct sunlight gets too warm, just under the surface of the water. These reptiles average about 10 feet in length and may live 100 years. *See page 1244*

Over 200 million years ago the turtle had become essentially what it is today, the changes in its structure during the incomprehensibly long period of time having been relatively minor. Whether they live in fresh or salt water or on land, turtles like crocodilians lay their eggs on land. They are most vulnerable while still in the egg and during the first few years while the shell is still soft, but once a turtle survives this critical time it can be expected to live a good 150 years.

See page 1250

[10-16]

[10-16A]

One turtle accident which can well prove fatal is for the creature to be flipped over on to its back. The protective shell in this case is a handicap as it seriously limits freedom of movement; many species, unable to right themselves, die of starvation and dehydration. The ornate box turtle is found in arid regions east of the Rocky Mountains and south into northern Mexico; other varieties of box turtles range from New England to Yucatan, Mexico. A dome-shaped reptile, its bottom shell is connected to the top part by bridges at the sides and is hinged at the front and back so that the turtle withdraws into a closed box.

See page 1253

The Fascination
of Flowers

CHILDREN love things that grow. That is probably why few toys can ever hold their attention as long as a garden will. Everything about a garden appeals to them. Planting a seed is a privilege they are ready to fight for, and day after day they will come back to see if it has begun to sprout. Watching a bud unfold is another experience that fills them with wonderment. It is no exaggeration to say that the youngster who does not have his own garden or flower box, or just a single flowerpot, is being deprived of one of childhood's most treasured possessions.

A child's interest in the plant world is by no means limited to flowers. Vegetables and flowerless plants, or even grass, will absorb his attention, too, and he will give them devoted care. What attracts him to plants is that they are living things, growing, expanding, changing.

Once your youngster becomes fully aware that plants have life just as animals do, a number of questions are bound to arise in his mind if he takes nature exploring seriously. Not so easy to answer as it is to ask is this one: "What's the difference between plants and animals?"

Plants Move Too. The younger child may be satisfied with the popular answer—quite oversimplified—that animals are capable of motion, moving from place to place by their own efforts—whereas plants cannot move. Often this answer will not do for an older child. As he thinks it over, he may realize that plants *do* move in certain ways.

For example, they move upward and outward as part of the growing process. Some develop runners that creep over the ground. Violets —and others—shoot their seeds; the dandelion is one of many plants that parachute seeds to new growing grounds, while portions of the stems of Florida moss break off and are blown about by the wind until they alight and start to grow. The water lily, like numerous other species, closes its petals each night and opens them again in the morning. (What probably impresses children even more is that the water lily floats.)

So we see there is plenty of motion on the part of plants. The older child will conclude that many characteristics observed in animals are also present in plants. Both plants and animals move; both are made up of living cells, are born, breathe, feed, grow, and reproduce themselves.

How Plants Feed Themselves. There is one vital difference between plants and animals, however, and that is in the way they feed themselves. A plant is in effect a factory which produces its own food *by turning non-living matter into living matter*. This process, one of Nature's wonders, is made possible by the green substance known as chlorophyll.

We often call chlorophyll "leaf-green", as it is found chiefly in leaves. When this leaf-green is worked on by the action of light from the sun, chemical changes occur which transform lifeless (inorganic) matter into life-giving and life-sustaining matter. (Animals do not have chlorophyll, but we now find it used in all kinds of products, from toothpaste to dog food, mainly for the purpose of killing odours.)

The Leaf—Nature's Great Chemical Laboratory

If you examine leaves, you will notice that as a rule they are a darker green on the upper side than on the underside. The chlorophyll-bearing cells on the top surface are packed more closely to catch as much sunlight as possible. (As we have seen, sunlight is one of the "raw materials" needed for making living matter.)

The "manufacturing" cells are protected on top and bottom surfaces by a skin, or epidermis, which is perforated with innumerable tiny holes. Each hole is surrounded by two guard-cells—the only surface cells that contain chlorophyll. Through the little holes the leaf constantly takes in and gives off oxygen, carbon dioxide, and other gases as well as water vapour.

HOW CHLOROPHYLL MAKES FOOD FOR PLANTS

Before the leaf "factory" can operate, it requires one more item. This is a watery solution, containing many substances, that originates in the soil, enters the plant roots, works its way up the stem and at last into the leaf.

Within each leaf, carbon dioxide—much of it comes from the air we exhale—is separated into carbon and oxygen. In the same way, water is broken down into oxygen and hydrogen. The leaf cells combine the carbon with the hydrogen and oxygen into a form of sugar that will nourish the plant. It is the chlorophyll that accomplishes this remarkable feat—but it can be done only when sunlight, or artificial light equal to sunlight, is shining on the plant.

In the daytime plants are our benefactors by releasing oxygen, which purifies the air we breathe. At night, though, they give off carbon dioxide, a gas which is poisonous when it is present in considerable quantity. (This explains why a room with many large house plants should be well aired at night.)

A scientist has estimated that during the course of a summer a single leaf, suitably exposed to sunlight, manufactures enough sugar to cover itself with a solid layer about one twenty-fifth of an inch thick—and this is apart from protein and other food elements that the plant needs.

Plants Turn Toward the Sun. Your house plants will give you a fine opportunity to observe how leaves are affected by the need for sunlight, in order to continue feeding the plants. Even a small child can observe how the location of the leaves at or near the ends of branches helps expose their surfaces to a maximum of light.

The youngster can also notice the way the plants sometimes change their position according to the direction of the source of light—and how, when a new length of stem grows, its young leaf bends and turns its stalk to escape, as much as possible, the shade of surrounding leaves. The leaves of nasturtiums, begonias, and others, are noticeably adept at keeping in a favourable light.

Out-of-doors there are some plants, such as one of the wild lettuces, which fix their leaves so consistently in a north-south plane that they are known as "compass plants".

Some "Dew" Doesn't Fall. Going out-of-doors in the early morning, a child always notices the dew, with some such exclamation as, "Look how much dew has fallen!" But like as not the drops of moisture he calls dew, did not "fall"; they are probably water that passed out of the grass and leaves as water vapour and condensed into drops as it emerged. If the night was humid and cool, the vapour could not become part of the air as rapidly as it came out of the leaves.

What Flowers Are For

There is much that a child can learn from house plants, but the real fun of studying flowers is mostly found outdoors. There he can watch insects travelling from one bloom to another in quest of nectar. As he observes flowers in numbers, he will see countless interesting variations in the shapes and colours of petals and in the forms of complete flowers. But there is a purpose in flowers beyond mere looks, beautiful though they are.

A child may be old enough to understand that what flowers are really for is to continue the life of the plants that bear them; yet, looking at a blooming garden, and with real curiosity in his voice, he will ask, "*How* do they?"

HOW FLOWERS DEVELOP SEEDS

A brief answer is that flowers produce seeds. But before a flower can produce seeds, it must receive grains of pollen that will fertilize it.

What is involved in the fertilization of a flower? To answer this

PETALS ARE A FLOWER'S CROWNING GLORY

The corolla (meaning "crown") of a flower may vary in countless ways. It is made up of petals, and these have numerous colours and shapes. Sometimes, too, each petal is separate (as in the lily, left); sometimes they are joined and show only as separate points (as in the squash flower, centre); and sometimes (as in the petunia, right) there is no separation whatever.

question, we must be familiar with the different parts that make up a flower.

Here a difficulty arises: not all flowers conform exactly to the same pattern.

Suppose, then, we consider the simplest types. One of these is the "perfect" flower—such as the lily—which has a pollen-bearing stamen and an ovary in which seeds develop.

The other simple type is a plant which bears two different types of flowers—the pussy willow is an example; one flower bears only the pollen-laden stamens while the other flower bears the ovary. In this case, we might call the flower with the stamens the "male" flower while the flower with the ovary is the "female" flower.

The Parts of a Flower and What They Do. It is a great help, in understanding how a flower functions, for a child to look at a diagram in which flower parts are pointed out. If he has a diagram illustrating a perfect flower, he will find:

The *ovary*—a well-protected structure in the centre of the flower. In it are

The *ovules*—which contain egg cells, destined to become seeds. (Some ovaries contain a single ovule; others have many ovules.) The ovary has a rather slender stalk, extending upward, and known as

The *style*. At its top, the style expands into a broadened tip with

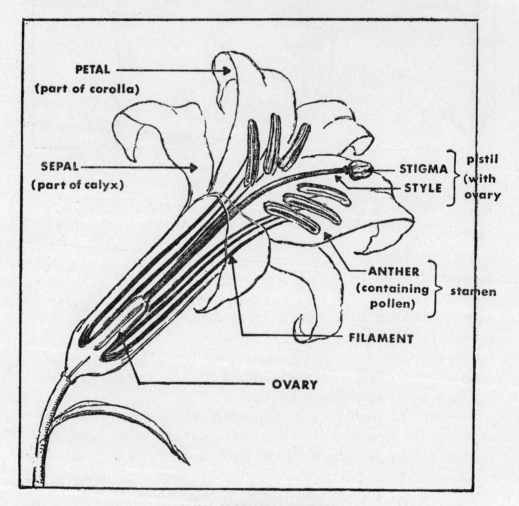

A SEED-PRODUCING FACTORY

All seeds are produced by flowers, but there is considerable variation in the forms of flowers. Not all types have both male parts (stamens) and female (pistil) within one blossom. Those that do are termed "perfect" flowers. This diagram of a lily (shown with transparent petals and sepals) illustrates one of them.

a sticky surface—a perfect trap for pollen. This expanded tip we call

The *stigma*. The combined stigma, style, and ovary form a complete *pistil*.

Also within the flower are

The *stamens*. A stamen consists of

The *filament*. This is a slender stalk, on the top of which rests

The *anther*, which encloses a powder (nearly always yellow) that we know as

The *pollen*. The pollen grains are formed by the division of cells within the anther. In our typical flower the pistil and the stamens are surrounded by

The *corolla*, composed of petals. This word, meaning "crown", is well chosen, for the corolla is the most beautiful part of the flower. In many flowers it is made up of separate petals; in other flowers— the squash flower, for one—the petals are joined together and show only as separate points. Then there are still other flowers—the petunia and morning-glory are among them—which have a corolla all in one piece, without any separation of the petals. In any event, the petals are encircled by

The *sepals*. All together, the sepals make up

The *calyx*, which serves to protect the flower, especially in its budding stage. The sepals, which are really specialized leaves, vary in size, shape, and number in different kinds of flowers. Often the sepals are green, as on the rose; but sometimes—as in the case of the tulip —you find them the same colour as the petals. On some kinds of plants sepals fall off as soon as the flower opens; on many others— roses and apple blossoms, for example—these leaves remain even after the seeds have ripened.

HOW THE SEED STARTS

The first step in the development of a seed is for pollen to reach the flower's stigma. The pollen may be blown into the stigma from the anther of some flower. What happens more commonly is that an insect, going from one flower to another in search of nectar, gets pollen on its body and the grains later rub off on a stigma.

Once a pollen grain has become attached to the sticky surface of the stigma, it quickly forms a tiny tube much like a root hair. This tube forces its way down the style to reach an egg cell in the ovule. As soon as the tube makes its connection with the egg cell, the life-germ in the pollen slips through the tube to combine with the life-germ in the egg cell. Thus the seed starts, developing on food furnished by the plant and on warmth given by the sun.

HOW THE SEED IS NOURISHED AND PROTECTED

A fully developed seed is the embryo of a new plant, with food stored around it in a form that can be used whenever new growth begins. One of the amazing things about seeds is that the stored food remains usable even though new growth does not start for weeks, months, or even years! (This dormant period varies, of course, with different kinds of seeds.) The embryo and the food supply are protected by one or more layers of the ovule.

Nuts and Tomatoes Are "Fruit". In some seeds, such as peas and beans, the food supply is stored within certain parts of the embryo itself. In other plants, corn and wheat for example, the food is stored around, rather than in, the embryo. And still other plants develop elaborate structures about their seeds. These structures are called "fruit"—apples and pears are familiar examples. When a scientist speaks of a "fruit", he may be referring to the ripened ovary of any kind of plant, be it the pod of a pea, a hard nut, or a juicy tomato.

There are many opportunities for examining seeds—for example, when you are preparing dinner. To a hungry diner, peas, beans, and corn are food; to a nature explorer, they are seeds! A child is thrilled to see the first sprouting of the plant embryo after he plants a few seeds in a glass with moist soil. If the seeds are placed just inside the glass, they can be seen sprouting.

HOW FLOWERS ATTRACT INSECTS

When a child learns that pollen is transferred from one plant to another by messenger insects, he may wonder what attracts an insect to flowers—is it their sweet scent or the colour of their petals? This is the kind of problem that scientists still ponder and sometimes debate about. For many years it was a generally accepted "fact" that the chief value of colour in flowers was to help to attract insects to them.

Scent Is the Attraction. Along came a scientist who had made a study of the insects' pollinizing role. He pointed out that bees and other flower-visiting insects have poor vision but a well-developed sense of smell. He also demonstrated that in addition to the colours that we can see, some flowers emit ultraviolet rays. Though these rays are not visible to our eyes, insects can see the rays as well as, or even better than, the colours which our eyes perceive. His over-all conclusion was that colour is, at most, only incidentally responsible for bringing insects to flowers.

Since that time, countless observations and experiments have shown that insects are attracted by the scent of flowers. In the course of one of his famous experiments, for example, Luther Burbank worked patiently to develop a petunia that would have fragrance. He knew that he had succeeded at last when he saw several bees hovering over one of the plants in a large bed of his experimental petunias. He quickly verified the fact that this particular plant's flowers *were* perfumed.

HOW POLLEN IS CARRIED FROM PLANT TO PLANT

It is vital for insects to visit flowers for, as we have seen, they carry pollen from plant to plant and thus help bring about the fertilization of flowers. Corn and all other plants known as "grasses", and most cone-bearing plants—such as pine trees—depend on the wind to convey their pollen.

Breeding Flowers. Sometimes man takes a hand in pollinating plants, especially when he wishes to create a hybrid, for a variety of reasons, by "crossing" the pollen of two different species in the same family. This may be done to increase the hardiness of a beautiful but fragile plant, or to make the colours of flowers more vivid.

Crossing different kinds of plants calls to mind the name of Luther Burbank. He will undoubtedly be remembered for all time as the great genius among plant breeders; it was he who made the science of "training plants to work for man" really practical.

He made countless improvements in vegetables as well as in flowers; bigger and better potatoes, sweet corn that matures early in the season, luscious blackberries on thornless bushes, and freestone plums of excellent flavour and texture, are just a few of them. There is no secret about the methods he used to bring about his "miracles" with plants.

These methods have often been described, and a book by Mr. Burbank (*Partner of Nature*) telling about his work is exciting reading.

How Seeds Are Scattered

One of the most intriguing aspects of the flower story involves the ways in which seeds are scattered. Many children get their first notion of seed dispersal when they blow at a dandelion "gone to seed". Each seed, attached to a filmy parachute, flies away.

Other times, say after a country hike, a youngster may find his clothes (or his dog's fur coat) covered with sticktights or cockleburs seeking transportation with their sharp little hooks. If he realizes these "burs" are seeds, unconsciously trying to use him or the dog as a means of reaching new growing grounds, he may find the job of prying them loose less tedious.

Other Ways That Seeds Travel. Although the seeds that are dispersed by the wind are the most conspicuous ones, we can observe other ways they travel. Some plants, including violets, pansies, and touch-me-nots, shoot their seeds. Water lilies and several other water plants bear seeds that manage to float to some desirable growing spot without becoming water-soaked.

180,000 *Seeds From a Plant.* Countless seeds are unsuccessful, as a youngster may realize when he throws the burs into a scrap basket; but this is of little importance as the number of seeds borne by each plant is incredibly large. Charles Darwin reported counting the seeds of an orchid; he found more than six thousand in a pod. As there were thirty pods on the plant, the total number of prospective seedlings from this parent would be something like 180,000!

A Garden of His Own

The modest blooms children raise themselves will easily thrill them as much as, if not more than, the most spectacular plants to be seen at a flower show. Window boxes and other indoor planting can give city youngsters some of the joy of raising plants; but families with land at their disposal have endless opportunity for engaging in one of the most solidly satisfying of all occupations—working in a garden.

An important point for you to bear in mind is that a youngster may be only casually interested in a family project—whereas if he is given a small plot of his own, the chances are that he will tend it with conscientious zeal. He enjoys having the power to decide what is to grow in that special piece of earth, he finds new delight in poring over seed packets and catalogues, and he is stimulated by the challenge of trying to bring his plans to a successful conclusion. He is not likely to ask for advice or help but he will probably welcome a little of each if it is offered tactfully.

ANNUALS, BIENNIALS, AND PERENNIALS

In planning his garden, a youngster will find annuals, biennials, and perennials from which to choose. Most plants that flower the same season they are sown are usually included with the annuals in flower books. However, the true annual is a plant that not only flowers the first season, but, if left to itself, dies in the autumn.

Biennial plants may flower during their first season, but more often do so the next year. Unless they are given special treatment by the gardener during their first season, biennials die after their second season.

Perennials—with the exception of woody types—die down to the ground in the autumn. But the roots continue to live, and new branches and flower stems are thrown up for years.

TREES, SHRUBS, AND HERBS

Another interesting point for the young gardener is that most flowering plants belong to one of three general forms: trees, which have large, erect stems; shrubs, with stems that are smaller and bushy;

and herbs, with stems that are more or less soft, and with little woody tissue. We most commonly use the term "herb" to describe plants valuable for medicinal purposes or for their flavour or sweet scent. Nevertheless, the majority of flowers (domesticated as well as wild), grasses, and weeds are herbs.

Favourite Flowers

FLOWERS FOR A BEGINNER

If you are a beginner, there are several points you will want to bear in mind. It is important to have plants that will thrive with the amount of sun that reaches the plot you are using. It is fun to have at least a few showy flowers—such as hollyhocks or salvia—as well as flowers good for cutting. Phlox, dianthus (pinks), zinnias, and asters are a few of the many that provide generous floral decoration for your home. Plants should be arranged so that those which grow tall will be at the back of the garden; the lowest ones should be in front, or else grown to form a border.

Plan Your Colour Scheme. Your child can begin to enjoy his garden well ahead of the planting season if he works out a "theme" for his plot. It may be an all-yellow colour scheme (marigolds, California poppies, nasturtiums, calliopsis); or purple and white (petunias, asters, baby's breath, hollyhocks); or red (salvia), white (petunia), and blue (ageratum). These flowers are a few of the many annuals from which a child should choose to obtain an abundance of blooms.

Protect the Seeds. If seeds are put in the earth too early they may freeze or rot. It is therefore advisable to start some annuals—pansies, for example—indoors or in a protected seed bed, and then move the young plants to the garden when the weather is suitable. Many flower enthusiasts eliminate this step by purchasing plants from commercial growers. Pansy plants produced from seeds planted outdoors do not bloom until the end of summer.

PANSIES—PERFECT FOR CHILDREN

Youthful gardeners can ask for no more delightful flower than the pansy. Its colouring is beautiful and its markings often give it an appealing face. The dark spots at the bases of the side petals and the lines radiating from them suggest eyes and eyelashes, the opening of the nectar tube makes a nose, and the spot near the base of the lower petal will pass for a mouth.

Many varieties of pansies may be easily raised from seed sown in the spring or early summer, and seedlings may be set out in the garden in early spring. They do better in shady areas than in full sunshine.

Pansies Are Ideal for Picking. Children love to pick flowers. This makes the pansy an ideal plant for a child, as the flowers should be picked as soon as they open, or shortly afterwards. If the pansy's seeds are allowed to ripen, the plant will bloom for only a short time, its life purpose having been accomplished. Persistent picking of the blooms, on the other hand, constantly produces new buds.

How Bees Help Fertilize the Pansy. The nectar sought by bees in the pansy is contained in the spur formed by the lower petal extending behind the flower. As the insect probes the nectar well with its tongue, pollen from a flower previously visited brushes off against the stigma. At the same time the bee receives a fresh coating of pollen dust. Shortly after a pansy has been fertilized, you can notice the ribbed seed pod becoming prominent. Finally this opens in three valves, and the seeds are scattered as the edges of each valve curl inward.

TULIPS—THE NATIONAL PASSION OF HOLLAND

This famous flower was introduced into Europe from the East in the sixteenth century, and about a hundred years later became the national passion of Holland. The Dutch growers speculated in outstandingly beautiful varieties of the tulip as some people speculate in stocks! Anyone who is familiar with these lovely flowers will understand the hold they took on Dutch tulip-fanciers.

Tulips Are Planted in the Autumn. Tulips are excellent material for youngsters who enjoy gardening in every season of the year. They may be put in the earth during September or October. Each bulb is formed of several layers of leaves, all of which may open above ground if the planting is done properly—with the tip of the bulb pointed upward. The leaf layers are fleshy, for they contain the food that was stored up during the previous season. This food nourishes the flower bud in the heart of each bulb and the other growing parts. The roots, forming a thick white tassel below the bud, bring minerals and water up from the soil.

The Tulip's Spring Buds. In the spring, the anxious gardener first sees his tulip buds appear, protected by three sepals. As the bud stretches upward and becomes larger, the green of the sepals changes to the colour of the petals. When the flower finally opens there is no very noticeable difference between petal and sepal. The sepals are below the petals and stand out around them, giving the flower a triangular shape. When the sun is not bright, the sepals partially close about the flower.

CORNFLOWERS—COMPOSITE FLOWERS

Most children love this hardy and beautiful plant; scientific name *centaurea*. It may have special interest for them, too, if they realize it is one of the "composite" plants—a group in which different kinds of flowers are attached to one head. Those at the centre of this compound flower head work for the production of seeds, while the flowers surrounding the centre serve merely to attract insects.

The cornflower head usually has from seven to fourteen marginal flowers and they may be white, pink, blue, or purple. Each of the centre flowers has a white corolla tube, enlarged toward the upper end to a purple bulb, and a purplish anther tube which is bent far over so that its tip opens toward the middle of the flower head.

GARDEN GERANIUMS—BUTTERFLIES' FAVOURITE

On no other flower will you see a more obvious nectar well; that of the geranium extends almost the whole length of the flower stalk. The long narrow nectar tube explains why you often see butterflies on geraniums; this shape is especially suitable for the long-tongued insects.

Some of these plants are called "horseshoe" geraniums because of the horseshoe pattern on many of the leaves. Botanically they are not true geraniums, being the descendants of the pelargonium—a plant that was brought to England from South Africa more than two hundred years ago. These African plants were the ancestors of many of our popular garden geraniums. Other varieties have been bred; Luther Burbank, for example, created the now popular crinkled-leaf species from a single wild geranium plant that did not have the customary smooth-edged leaves.

Seeds Spread by Explosion. Some geraniums have depended for so long on man for planting that they have almost lost the power of producing seed. However, in the single blossoms you may sometimes discover the ovary changed into a long beaklike seed pod—a feature that reveals its relationship to the wild geranium. The seeds are dispersed by an explosive action of the pod.

How Geraniums Open. It is interesting to watch geranium flowers opening. Several buds are grouped together in a nest of specialized leaves known as bracts. Besides having this protection, each bud is individually guarded by its own sepals. As the flower stalk grows longer and droops from the weight of the buds, the bracts often fall off. In each mass of drooping buds, the ones in the centre open first. It sometimes happens that by the time those on the outside are in bloom the centre flowers have begun to wither.

NASTURTIUMS AND THEIR REMARKABLE METHOD OF POLLINATION

The most remarkable aspect of the nasturtium is its special method of pollination. The five beautiful petals are set around the mouth of the long tube leading to the nectar well. The two upper petals are erect, suggesting colourful display signs. They are marked with lines that point toward the opening of the nectar tubes. The lower petals stand out to form a landing platform for visiting insects.

Despite this, the flower is not actually designed for hospitality; it can accommodate only big insects such as sizable bees or butterflies for its pollination work, and it is able to thwart smaller, useless creatures that might creep into its treasure house of nectar. Each of the lower "landing" petals narrows to a fine strip at its inner end, making it in effect a footbridge to the nectar tube. These bridges are covered with projecting fringes and numerous little spikes that prove an effective barrier to any small creeping visitors.

Mechanized Pollination. When a nasturtium first opens, its several stamens are all bent downward. But when the pollen-containing anthers—located at the end of each slender stalk of a stamen—are ready to function, the stalk lifts up so that it is directly in the path of the nectar store. When a bee or butterfly, or occasionally a humming-bird, touches the stamens, it is sometimes bombarded with pollen. Equally remarkable is the action of the anther: no sooner has it discharged its pollen than it shrivels, making way for a new anther.

While all this is going on, the flower's three-lobed stigma lies quietly below and behind the anthers. (The stigma is located on the prolongation of the ovary known as the style.) But, once all the pollen has been shed, the stigma rises up and opens. Now the stigma operates like a three-pronged fork, and as more insects come in quest of nectar, it rakes pollen from them. Thus the ovary is fertilized and the seeds are ready to develop.

PETUNIAS AND THEIR INTERNATIONAL BACKGROUND

Profusely blooming petunias are so much a part of the garden scene that it comes as a surprise to us to learn that they have an international background. They are the result of a cross between two species of plants from different parts of South America. The first of these, with long-tubed white flowers, was brought to Europe a little more than a hundred years ago. Shortly afterwards seeds of the second species, having small, broad-tubed, red-purple flowers, were sent to the Glasgow Botanical Gardens where the two species were brought together. Today we find petunias of many colours, but red-purple and white still predominate.

Pollen for Petunias. The petunia's wonderful arrangement for pollination is one of the marvels of Nature. Near the bottom of the long tube lies the stigma, with two well-developed anthers in front of it and two more—not quite so advanced—behind it. The stalks that support the front anthers are longer than those of the second pair.

There is still another anther—a fifth—on a stalk shorter than all the others. This is apparently a little pollen supply held in reserve by the flower.

For about half its length, each stamen is attached to the base of the flower's tube. The rest of the stamen curves abruptly inward. This makes it snuggle up to the pistil, the base of which is set in the nectar well at the bottom of the flower. When an insect pays a visit, its tongue reaches along the flower tube toward the nectar and it presses against the stamens at the point where they curve. This causes the anthers to move about, and as they move their pollen is shaken off on to the insect!

In an older petunia the stigma, standing above the empty antlers, opens into two lobes and is ready to receive pollen from other flowers.

The Petunia and the Humming-bird Moth. The most notable insect partners of petunias are the sphinx or humming-bird moths, which can often be seen hovering over these flowers in the early evening. Petunias are members of the "nightshade" family, which also includes the tomato, the potato, and tobacco. Humming-bird moths are distinctly partial to all these plants.

POPPIES—THEY FASCINATE BEES

The poppy is distinctly a bee's flower. The insects apparently delight in wallowing in the pollen that lies along the ridges of the flower's pistil.

This pistil resembles a tiny vase with a circular cover. After a poppy has been fertilized, the circular cover develops a scalloped edge. Sharp ridges run from the centre of each scallop down the length of the vaselike pistil. These ridges are the outer edges of partitions. Countless seeds develop inside these partitions and, when ripe, they fall into the hollow capsule which forms the centre of the pistil.

The Poppy's Seed-Shaker. An observant child is charmed to see how poppy seeds make their way in the world. As each segment of the capsule loosens at the top and curls back from the circular cover, openings are formed. The upshot is that the "vase" has been made into a perfect seed-shaker. When the wind blows on it, or when it is brushed by any passing creature, the contents—the seeds—are sprinkled a little at a time in all directions.

There are a great many varieties of poppies, but only four species are commonly cultivated: the corn poppy and the opium (both of them annuals); the Arctic and the Oriental (both perennials).

The California poppy in its native setting blooms abundantly from February to April in the desert and the foothills. In gardens in the East you can see the shining orange flowers from mid-summer until frost arrives.

IRISES—LARGE AND SHOWY

The large, showy iris, also called "blue flag," is another plant favoured by bees. It has an interesting shape because of its unique style, which is divided into three branches so large and broad that they appear to be petals. These branches combined with the sepals form a tunnel through which bees pass. Between the sepals and the styles are the true petals, marked with decorative purple lines.

How the Bee Manoeuvres on the Iris. The bee uses the lip of a sepal for its landing platform, then pushes forward through the tunnel to the nectar well. As the insect moves, pollen that it has collected from another flower is rubbed off against the stigma, which hangs like a tent flap above the nectar well. The stigma is so fashioned that it gathers pollen from an incoming insect but turns a blank side to the departing visitor.

The small solitary bees are persistent callers; so are bumblebees and honeybees, though they seem to prefer different varieties of the iris.

ROSES—THE WORLD'S MOST POPULAR FLOWERS

It has been said that children see so many roses that they take them for granted. I doubt that this is really their attitude, as so many of them choose roses when asked to write about their favourite nature subject. Certainly the rose appears to be the world's most popular flower.

It is grown wherever gardening is practised, in all temperate climates and in some tropical regions as well. It is also believed to be the oldest of cultivated flowers.

Though no flower is more readily identified, many people are perplexed by the question, "What *is* a rose?" Looking for an answer, we may be inclined to find more sense than nonsense in Gertrude Stein's famous statement, "A rose is a rose is a rose"; for the rose has endless varieties and it is neither an ordinary seed plant nor a tree. There are single blooms, having only one row of showy petals, and double blooms with their rows of petals arranged in regular sequence or in loose informal patterns.

Five Thousand Varieties of Roses. The roses' bright colours cover a wide range from white, through delicate pink, yellow to rich tones of red. As to size, they vary from miniatures as small as a sixpence to exhibition blooms seven inches and more across. Believe it or not, in the United States alone there are more than five thousand varieties, each differing in some detail. The plant is a woody shrub which may stand erect or climb on supports. It has an extensive root system that sometimes goes as deep as twenty feet into the ground.

Roses and Strawberries Are Relatives. Apart from the innumerable kinds of roses produced in gardens, there is the simple but very beautiful wild rose with its broad blossoms that display five pink petals. On a wild rose or a full-blown garden rose you can easily see the great number of stamens, about twenty, as a rule, a characteristic feature of the whole family. Usually there are a great many pistils also.

Many of our common fruits belong to the rose family; the plants include the creeping strawberry as well as the sturdy blackberry bush and apple tree. Though these plants differ considerably in size and general appearance, their blossoms have a great similarity to the rose.

CHRYSANTHEMUMS—JAPANESE FAVOURITE

The chrysanthemum has a double flower head, numerous petals, and lovely colouring (generally red, yellow, and white). It gets wide publicity every autumn as the star attraction of countless flower shows. But it is not only the spectacular prize-winning varieties that merit popularity. There are many kinds that will flourish without highly skilled care, bringing fresh beauty to our gardens in the autumn when most flowers are dying.

Until fairly recently "mums" could be grown in northern climates only inside a greenhouse; but now we have hardy types that bloom out-of-doors through light frost. These perennials usually survive the winter, and each spring you can separate the new growths and re-plant them. Thus your chrysanthemum display can expand considerably from a very few plants.

Two Thousand Years of Chrysanthemums. Two thousand years ago, a chrysanthemum much like a coloured daisy was a popular garden flower in Japan. (A figure of a sixteen-petalled chrysanthemum is used as the crest of the Japanese Imperial family.) Early in the eighteenth century some of these flowers were brought to England, and China and India contributed other species. English gardeners and plant breeders went to work with them and in less than a hundred years produced new varieties bearing flowers three times as large as any of the originals.

DAHLIAS—THEY GROW EVEN ON ASH HEAPS

The dahlia, a reddish flower that originated in Mexico and Central America, is a popular show flower. Because of their size and beauty, you might suspect that dahlias are difficult to raise. The fact is, though, that dahlias are adaptable to almost any kind of soil, if it has been properly prepared.

Clayey soil may be lightened with coal ashes or sand, plus vegetable matter and manure. A light sandy loam will produce healthy plants and exquisite blooms; gravelly fields have been known to support fine dahlia beds; and a plant may even be found growing in an ash heap where a tuber (the underground stem) has been discarded.

How to Protect Dahlia Seeds. You can raise dahlias from stem cuttings as well as from tubers. For a real gardening adventure, your youngster may enjoy trying to develop new dahlias from seeds. The project begins at the height of the blooming season, when he must be on the lookout for any particularly large, rich-coloured flower. This should be tagged "For Seed", so that it will not be picked.

The chosen flower must now remain in the garden until insects have carried pollen to it and it "goes to seed". When the flower shrivels and turns brown, you tie a small paper bag over it so that you can save the seeds if the seed pod bursts.

How to Plant Dahlia Seeds. Late autumn is the time for you to gather the seeds, drying them and storing them in an airtight bottle. Early in May you plant them in a box with one part soil to two parts sand mixture. When seedlings appear about two weeks later, transplant them to a sunny spot in the garden.

Until the buds finally open, the young gardener will go through the suspense of wondering whether they will be double or single flowers and what their colour will be. It all depends on what pollen was carried to his flowers during the previous season.

Indoor Gardening

If you live in an apartment and cannot have a garden outdoors, you and your child can share the rich pleasures of starting a garden indoors. Bulbs are especially suitable. (Bulbs are buds made up of a stem surrounded by leaves.) You can buy them inexpensively at many department stores, hardware stores, or florist shops.

Narcissus Bulbs Are Easy to Grow. The narcissus, a popular favourite with yellow or white varieties, need only be supported in a shallow dish with pebbles or bits of broken shell, and given just enough water to show through the pebbles.

Unaided, a youngster can easily prepare a dish for a narcissus bulb, and will be thrilled at having something his very own. To enhance his enjoyment, a narcissus grows rapidly and thus rewards daily watching. Care should be taken when watering that water does not leak in where old leaves have broken off, as this causes a bulb to rot.

When it is first planted, the bulb should be kept in a dark cool place until its roots have formed. Outdoors this would take from eight to twelve weeks, but indoors only a few weeks are required. The plant should then be brought into sunlight gradually, being kept away from draughts. Two or three weeks will elapse before a flower appears.

Hyacinth, Tulip, and Crocus Bulbs. Such bulbs as hyacinths and tulips do better in soil. As bulbs have a built-in food supply, the soil need not be rich. Sandy garden soil well mixed with peat moss is excellent. A hyacinth bulb should be placed so that its top projects over the top of the pot; a tulip bulb should have its top level with the top of the soil. As for crocus and other small bulbs, they should be covered with an inch of soil.

If you keep the bulbs in a cool dark place for several weeks, the roots will be well developed before the leaf stalks begin properly to grow.

When the roots press against the sides of the pot or show at the bottom opening, you know that the plants are ready for a sunny window.

OTHER EASY INDOOR GARDENING TECHNIQUES

You need not limit your indoor gardening to bulbs. You have the choice of plants growing directly from roots or from stem cuttings—begonia, geranium, or cactus, among others; and from certain fleshy leaves, such as those of the African violet. Also, many seeds thrive when they are planted indoors.

A wooden cigar box will do to give stem cuttings or leaves their start. Bore holes in the bottom and spread pebbles or chips from broken flowerpots. Then fill the box with clean sand to within half an inch of the top. Moisten the sand and press it down firmly. Make a hole in this soil for each stem cutting you wish to plant. (A pencil is a very good tool for this purpose.)

Now place a freshly cut stem in each hole, making sure that in every case you have buried at least two "nodes"—juncture points for leaves that have been removed. Keep the little garden moist, in a cool place, and before long, roots should form at each node.

How to Propagate Plants

AFRICAN VIOLETS

You can work out an excellent arrangement for propagating African violets from leaves by using two flowerpots—one an eight-inch size and shallow, the other a three-inch pot. Cover the hole of the larger pot with a piece of crockery and partly fill the pot with sand. Close the hole of the smaller pot with a cork, and place this pot inside the larger one, filling the space between the two pots with more sand. If you keep the small flowerpot filled with water, the sand will be moist at all times. Set the base of the violet leaves in the moistened sand.

BEGONIAS AND SNAKE PLANTS

Begonia leaves may simply be pegged down with toothpicks on moist sand and slit across the main veins. Small plants will develop at the wounds. The ever-popular snake plant, or Sansevieria, may be propagated by cutting leaves into sections an inch or more in length and pegging them into moist earth. The leaves of this white or yellowish plant take root easily but grow slowly.

Any plant you are raising from leaves or stems should be covered by a glass jar or globe until it has become well rooted. The covering keeps the air immediately surrounding the plants moist; an excessively dry atmosphere would soon kill them.

GROWING FLOWERS INDOORS

If flowers interest you more, you will find that marigolds, petunias, and other plants will flourish in your window boxes. Smaller seeds should be planted about a quarter of an inch deep, and larger ones slightly deeper; allow at least an inch between seeds. When your seedlings are large enough to handle, transplant them to window boxes or flowerpots.

Vegetables—for Decoration and Food

WORKING WITH SEEDS

If you wish to work with seeds, you will need a shallow tray with holes in the bottom (for drainage) to start your gardening. Place small stones or pieces of broken flowerpots over the holes; then sift soil into the box and press down firmly until the soil is within an inch of the top. If you want to try a miniature vegetable garden, you can plant such seeds as peas, beans, and radishes.

GROWING DANDELION GREENS

A child who shows real enthusiasm for gardening may derive great pleasure from growing a few indoor "crops" during the winter which may be used on family menus. However, a warm cellar is usually essential for such activity. There are several plants that will flourish in a box of earth set beside a furnace. Dandelion greens, which are a tasty substitute for lettuce, are among the easiest to obtain and raise.

Dig up the plants, including roots, before the ground freezes, and cut off a good two inches of the leafy top. Then set the roots in a box of good garden soil, and keep them in a constantly warm location—if possible, near a furnace. They require some watering but need no light.